Understanding Biblical Doctrine

A Workbook in Theology

Crown & Covenant
PUBLICATIONS

Crown & Covenant Publications
7408 Penn Avenue
Pittsburgh PA 15208-2531
412-241-0436, Fax: 412-731-8861

info@crownandcovenant.com

www.crownandcovenant.com

ISBN-13: 978-1-884527-17-3
ISBN-10: 1-884527-17-3

Understanding Biblical Doctrine

Table of Contents

Preface

Understanding Biblical Doctrine was written by Ronald W. Nickerson some thirty years ago when he served as director of publications for the Reformed Presbyterian Church of North America. Over the years, it has proved to be a popular workbook on the basic teaching of the Bible and a faithful witness to the mission of our church.

From time to time, "U.B.D." (as it is affectionately called among us) has been gently revised to reflect developments in the church and its ministry. The need for a somewhat more thorough update became apparent as the new millennium dawned, and the editors are pleased to present a new and improved edition for a new generation.

Here you will find what is commonly called "the Reformed Faith"—the teaching of Jesus and the apostles as recovered at the Protestant Reformation and believed by generations of Christians across the globe ever since. Here also are those aspects and applications of biblical faith that are dear to Reformed Presbyterians. The study ends with the personal covenant of Thomas Boston, a minister of the Church of Scotland from 1699 until his death in 1732. But this is really where we begin with the Lord—in personal covenant with God in His Son, Jesus, received as our Savior. *Understanding Biblical Doctrine* is about new life, eternal life, through faith in a living, risen Savior. May the Lord bless these studies to your growth in grace and in the knowledge of our Lord Jesus Christ.

—*The Editors*

Acknowledgments

Special thanks to Pastors Douglas Comin and Gordon Keddie for their help in developing this edition.

Before We Start...

While we often hear of those who accept a certain teaching "because the church says so," this workbook seeks to show how doctrines are properly derived from the Bible itself. This emphasis prevails while unfolding the system of doctrine expressed in the *Westminster Confession of Faith,* the *Westminster Larger* and *Shorter Catechisms,* and the *Testimony of the Reformed Presbyterian Church of North America.* These doctrinal aids are commonly referred to as subordinate standards, meaning that they are the carefully determined formulations and applications of the doctrines of the Bible, but are never to be put on a par with Scripture. They are to lead us back to God's Word, not to take its place.

Each lesson contains simple exercises to familiarize users with key passages of Scripture and questions to stimulate discussion. Because of its widespread availability, the *New King James Version* of the Bible is directly employed but use of other translations is strongly urged. Those conducting these studies are expected to engage in outside preparation. Suggestions for digging deeper are provided. Each unit should provide approximately one hour of discussion, but leaders should be sensitive to the needs of the group and be ready to expand or contract accordingly. The person with high school training should be able to understand all the basic concepts presented. Those with greater formal education should be challenged by directed readings and more intensive discussion.

'Doctrine' isn't a dirty word

Why study doctrine? "I can't see any point to learning all those doctrines. What really counts is the way Christians *live.* We have too much arguing in the church already." Does this sound familiar to you? Many sincere Christians hold this position, which might be diagrammed like this:

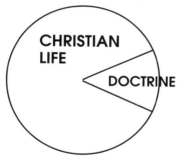

They consider doctrine to be "dead orthodoxy." For them the heart of Christianity lies in its practice, not its teaching. As a result, these believers are often weak in their understanding of Scripture, unable to grasp the "strong meat" of the Word. And yet Jesus insists that it is our *faith* that saves, not our works. And Paul says it is necessary to know the *whole counsel of God,* not simply a few basic beliefs.

Doctrine determines life

The fact is that there can be no true godliness without sound knowledge of Scripture. Jesus taught that it is the *truth* that makes us free, and by "truth" He clearly meant the truth of God's revealed Word (John 8:31-32). We might diagram the idea this way:

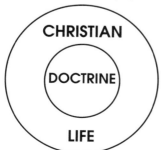

The essence of this view is that *doctrine determines life.* We cannot please God unless we first understand what He reveals to us in His Word as His plan and purpose. Whereas the view above stresses man's works and man himself as the central focus of Christianity, the Reformed faith centers on the sovereignty of God, the grace found in Christ Jesus, and the truth revealed by the Holy Spirit. Such a perspective leads then to the highest regard for the authority of Scripture as the only rule of faith and life given us whereby we may glorify and enjoy God.

This manual adopts the stance of those who accept the Reformed faith. Scripture is set forth as the single infallible source of Christian doctrine. Because the Bible is a progressive revelation of God's truth, it is necessary to compile and compare passages that deal with basic doctrinal questions. This task is commonly called *systematic theology*. Its goal is to set down in orderly fashion the major teachings of the Bible to aid us in being able to "give a reason for the hope that is in us" and to "know what is that good and acceptable and perfect will of God" so that our lives may reflect that perfect obedience Christ desires in His own.

The heavy use of "proof texts" in the exercises is not intended to oversimplify the development of doctrine, but to acquaint the learner with those key passages of Scripture which are the basis of concrete theological discussion. The leader is expected to fill in the Biblical context of verses quoted. While God's Word is a fixed and fully authoritative revelation; nowhere is it to be assumed that our *understanding* of biblical doctrine is infallible. The Christian church is ever to search Scripture to expand, refine, restate, and, if necessary, to change certain of her doctrinal tenets in the light of her continued study of Scripture.

Digging Deeper

The Westminster Confession of Faith, G.I. Williamson, 2nd ed., 2004, Presbyterian & Reformed, 409 pp.

Systematic Theology, Louis Berkhof, Eerdmans, 1996, 784 pp.

Revelation & Inspiration

Memorize

John 20:31
But these are written that you may believe that Jesus is the Christ, the Son of God, and that believing you may have life in His name.

Shorter Catechism
Q. 2: What rule hath God given to direct us how we may glorify and enjoy him?
A: The Word of God, which is contained in the Scriptures of the Old and New Testaments, is the only rule to direct us how we may glorify and enjoy him.

Q. 3: What do the Scriptures principally teach?
A: The Scriptures principally teach, what man is to believe concerning God, and what duty God requires of man.

Suggested Readings
Confession of Faith—Chapter 1
Reformed Presbyterian Testimony—Chapter 1

What Do You Think About the Bible?
(The word "Bible" here means the original manuscripts.)

Do You Think That:

_____1. The Bible is true in matters of faith, but may contain slight errors in history?

_____2. We can learn that God is a Trinity of Persons without consulting the Bible?

_____3. Verbal inspiration means that each and every word of the Bible was directly dictated by God and that the human writers served mainly as stenographers?

_____4. The King James Version is the infallible word of God?

_____5. The New Testament is more valuable than the Old Testament?

_____6. A person can have saving faith in Christ without believing the Bible to be true?

_____7. We are able to accept the Scriptures as God's Word because they satisfy our ability to reason?

_____8. God does not speak to men today apart from Scripture?

_____9. The only evidence we have that God exists is the record of Him in the Bible?

_____10. Evangelical Christians believe that every statement in the Bible must be believed *literally?*

Choose the Best Answer

1. Verbal inspiration means:
   a. the truths of the Bible are infallible, but expressed in men's words.
   b. the words of the Bible in the original manuscripts are without error.
   c. God inspired men to write down their religious ideas to share with others.

2. The Bible is:
   a. the only revelation of God to man.
   b. the only infallible rule of faith and life for Christians today.
   c. one of the best ways God speaks to men today.

3. The writers of Scripture:
   a. expressed their personalities in their writings, but were kept from error by the Holy Spirit.
   b. were like secretaries taking direct dictation from God.
   c. received God's perfect truth and put it into their own words, which are not perfect.

4. The Old and New Testaments:
   a. include the Word of God.
   b. reveal the basic ideas of God.
   c. are the Word of God.

5. The Bible is truly inspired because:
   a. it is the most reasonable explanation of God and humanity.
   b. it is the self-authenticating Word of God.
   c. it inspires everyone who reads it with an open mind.

Revelation

Definition: Revelation refers to the means by which God has chosen to make known His person, activities, and will to the human race.

God reveals Himself in His creation.

This is commonly known as *general* or *natural* revelation. It is sufficient to make every man aware of God's existence, but it does not reveal the Triune God and His acts in the salvation of men and women.

1. Psalm 19:1-4

   a. What do the heavens declare to all of us?

   _____

   _____

b. What does verse 2 say is shown to us by the creation?

_____

c. How widespread (v. 3) is the testimony of God in nature?

_____

2. Romans 1:18-20

a. How is the unbeliever described in verse 18 concerning his knowledge of God's truth?

_____

b. How does verse 20 state that God has made Himself and His invisible characteristics known to all?

_____

c. What are we able to perceive about God from His creation (v. 20)?

_____

d. What is the result upon us all of this universal knowledge of God (v. 20)?

_____

God reveals Himself savingly in *special* revelation.

This is also known as supernatural revelation and refers to the particular means by which God has revealed Himself and His will to sinful men in order to acquaint them with His Covenant of salvation through Jesus Christ. Complete the following matching exercise as a means to acquaint yourself with the forms God's special revelation has taken since mankind's fall into sin. Match the appropriate verses listed in the right-hand column to the form of revelation in the left-hand column.

God has revealed Himself:

_____1. in direct appearance (theophany)   a. Heb. 1:1

_____2. in a voice from heaven   b. Matt. 3:17

_____3. in dreams or visions   c. 2 Tim. 3:16

_____4. in His Son, Jesus Christ   d. John 2:23

_____5. by the Prophets   e. Deut. 5:4

_____6. by the Apostles   f. Heb. 1:2

_____7. through His miracles   g. Acts 11:5

_____8. by the Scriptures   h. Eph. 3:5

The Authority of Scripture

Definition: The original manuscripts of the Old and New Testaments are given by God the Holy Spirit in a way that makes them free from error but at the same time does not rule out the personality and style of the individuals chosen by God to write His Word. This is commonly referred to as verbal or organic inspiration.

The Bible is inspired by God. (This means that the Scripture has as its final source and authority the person and mind of God.)

    1.   2 Timothy 3:15-16

        a.   What is the primary purpose of the Bible as it is stated in verse 15?

_____

_____

        b.   How is Scripture given to us?

_____

_____

        c.   What are the four uses of Scripture stated in verse 16?

_____

        Note: The words "given by inspiration" in verse 16 are better translated as "God-breathed."

    2.   2 Peter 1:21

        a.   What did *not* produce true prophecies in Old Testament times?

_____

        b.   How did true prophecy come about?

_____

_____

        Note: The word "moved" here signifies a special protection and guiding of the author's words by God, *not* a mechanical dictation.

The Bible has full authority as God's Word.

    1.   Psalm 31:5; Deuteronomy 32:4; John 17:17—What common quality is attributed to both God and His Word?

_____

2. Leviticus 19:2 and Romans 7:12—What common quality is attributed in these verses to both God and His Word?

    _____

3. Matthew 5:17 and John 10:35—What is Jesus' view of the Old Testament as expressed in these verses?

    _____

4. 1 Thessalonians 2:13—How did the Thessalonians receive the message preached by the Apostle Paul?

    _____

The Bible is sufficient as the only rule of faith and life.

1. Proverbs 30:6

    a. What is commanded against?

        _____

    b. What is the punishment for disregarding this command?

        _____

2. Revelation 22:18-19

    a. What is forbidden in verse 18?

        _____

    b. What is forbidden in verse 19?

        _____

The Bible is self-authenticating. It is not to be verified by anything (e.g. man's power to reason) lower than itself.

1. Psalm 19:7-9—List the seven adjectives that state the claim the Bible makes concerning its own character:

    _____

    _____

    _____

    _____

9

2. Psalm 19:7-9—List the four phrases that state what the Bible is designed to do for the believer:

_____

_____

_____

_____

The Bible is life-changing.

Psalm 19:10-11—What three effects does it have in the Christian's experience?

_____

_____

For Discussion*

1. What role does fulfilled prophecy play in showing the authority of Scripture as God's Word?

2. Should we be concerned whether or not archeology supports the historical parts of the Bible?

3. What does 1 Corinthians 2:12-16 have to say about our ability to prove to unbelievers that the Bible is true?

4. How reliable are the Bible translations we use? Is it still proper to say that we have God's infallible truth when we don't know Greek and Hebrew?

5. In what practical ways have you discovered that the authority of Scripture goes head-to-head against the world?

*Leaders, see supplement.

Digging Deeper...

1. J.C. Ryle, *"How Readest Thou?" An Urgent Appeal to Search the Scriptures,* Moscow, Id., 62 pp. *A wonderful read from a classic preacher!*

2. Roger Ellsworth, *The Guide to the Bible Book by Book,* Evangelical Press, 432 pp. *A book that succinctly expounds the great theme of God's Word—the message of salvation by grace in Jesus Christ.*

3. Brian H. Edwards, *Nothing But the Truth,* Evangelical Press, 392 pp. *The inspiration, authority, and history of the Bible simply explained.*

The Nature of God

> **Memorize**
>
> John 4:24
> *"God is Spirit, and those who worship Him must worship in spirit and truth."*
>
> Shorter Catechism
> *Q 4: What is God?*
> *A: God is a Spirit, infinite, eternal, and unchangeable, in his being, wisdom, power, holiness, justice, goodness, and truth.*

Suggested Readings

Confession of Faith - Chapter 2
Reformed Presbyterian Testimony - Chapter 2

What Do You Think About God?

Do You Think That:

_____ 1. God is one Person who reveals Himself in three different ways, like a man who can be a father, a son, and a brother at the same time?

_____ 2. The Trinity is not taught in the Bible?

_____ 3. Jesus is equal in power and authority with God the Father?

_____ 4. God's omnipotence gives Him power over all His creation?

_____ 5. God is pure spirit without a body?

_____ 6. God can be completely loving and completely just at the same time?

_____ 7. The Holy Spirit is merely a divine force for good in our lives, not a Person?

_____ 8. Because God is not subject to time and so knows all things all at once, we may describe His existence as an "eternal now"?

_____ 9. God the Father existed before God the Son?

_____ 10. The Bible tells us everything there is to know about God and His ways?

The Nature (essence) of God

God is a pure Spirit.

1. John 4:24—How does Jesus describe the nature of God here?

    _____

2. Acts 17:24—What does Paul say God does not do?

    _____

God is a personal being.

1. Psalm 25:8—What aspects of God's personality are given here?

    _____

2. John 3:16—What personal trait of God is stated here?

    _____

God is a triune being. (Three persons, yet one God united in the Godhead)

1. The trinitarian nature of God is *progressively* revealed in the Old Testament.

    a. *the majestic plural*—Genesis 1:1-3, 26

        How does God refer to Himself in these verses?

        _____

    b. *the Angel of the Lord* (an Old Testament prefiguring of God's salvation through the pre-incarnate Christ)

        1) Genesis 32:30—What does Jacob say about his encounter with the Angel at Peniel?

            _____

        2) Genesis 48:16—What did Jacob say the Angel had done for him?

            _____

    c. *the plurality of God's being in the Psalms*

        1) Psalm 2:2, 7, 12

            a) What two persons are mentioned in verse 2?

                _____

b) What relationship is presented in verse 7?

_____

c) What does it mean to "kiss the Son" in verse 12?

_____

d) In verse 12, in whom are we told to put our trust?

_____

Does Scripture ever command us to trust anyone who is less than wholly divine?

_____

2) Psalm 110:1-7

a) In verse 1, what two persons are mentioned?

_____

b) In verse 4, what has God promised that is true of Jesus Christ (see Heb. 2:17)?

_____

2. The Trinity is revealed *by deed* in the New Testament. (The writers of the New Testament did not write theological defenses of the Trinity; they simply recorded those acts that indicate the existence and equal authority of the Father, Son, and Spirit.)

a. *at the Baptism of Jesus*—Matthew 3:16-17
State how the three Persons of the Trinity are present here?

_____

b. *at the end of Christ's earthly ministry*—Matthew 28:19
How is baptism to be administered?

_____

Note: The fact that there is *one* "name" indicates the equality of authority in the Persons involved as well as their oneness in the Godhead.

c. *in the ministry of the Apostles*—2 Corinthians 13:14

Whom does Paul call upon to bless the Corinthian Christians?

_____

13

Exercise: In the list of God's attributes given below, write in the most appropriate text beside each attribute. No text listed need be used more than once.

John 3:16   Isa. 40:18   James 1:17   Matt. 19:26   Isa. 6:3
Ps. 7:9   Ps. 139:7-10   Deut. 6:4   1 Sam. 2:3   Ps. 31:5
Rom. 11:22   1 Cor. 2:7   Dan. 4:35

The Attributes (characteristics) of God

Incommunicable (unique to God with no resemblance in created humans)

1. total independence (self-existence) _____

2. immutability (unchangeableness) _____

3. infinity (timelessness and spacelessness which is called His omnipresence) _____

4. simplicity (God is totally one, the whole being of God belongs to each one of His Persons)

_____

Communicable (some resemblances found in man's personality)

1. knowledge (ability to understand all things or His omniscience) _____

2. wisdom (employment of all the knowledge at God's command) _____

3. goodness (graciousness to others) _____

4. love (compassion and pure affection) _____

5. holiness (moral perfection) _____

6. righteousness (just dealings with men) _____

7. truth (faithfulness to His Word) _____

8. sovereignty (God's exercise of His will as the final cause of all things) _____

9. omnipotence (God's complete power over all things) _____

For Discussion

1. How do we explain Old Testament references to the "eyes" and "hands" of God if God has no body? What is anthropomorphism?

2. Is it possible to prove the Trinity scientifically?

3. Is it necessary to believe in the Trinity to be saved?

4. What sects today teach that Jesus is less than the eternal Son of God, equal with the Father in substance, power and authority?

5. How does an improper understanding of God affect our lives and our worship?

Digging Deeper...

1. John Blanshard, *Is God Past His Sell-by Date?*, Evangelical Press, 268 pp. *A very readable treatment of the existence of God.*

2. G. I. Williamson, *The Westminster Confession of Faith*, Presbyterian & Reformed, chap. 2. *An eminently useful commentary on the* Westminster Confession.

3. Gordon H. Clark, *The Trinity*, Trinity Foundation, 157 pp. *A clear and concise treatment of the doctrine of God in three Persons throughout the history of the Church.*

Man's Origin & Nature

Memorize

Genesis 1:27
So God created man in His own image; in the image of God He created him; male and female He created them.

Romans 3:23
For all have sinned and fall short of the glory of God . . .

Shorter Catechism
Q. 1: *What is the chief end of man?*
A: *Man's chief end is to glorify God, and to enjoy him for ever.*

Q. 9: *What is the work of creation?*
A: *The work of creation is, God's making all things of nothing, by the word of his power, in the space of six days, and all very good.*

Q. 14: *What is sin?*
A: *Sin is any want of conformity unto, or transgression of, the law of God.*

Suggested Readings
Confession of Faith—Chapters 4, 6–7
Reformed Presbyterian Testimony—Chapters 4, 6–7

Who Do You Think You Are?

Do You Think That:

_____ 1. The Bible teaches that the six days of creation were each of normal length?

_____ 2. God made the heavens and the earth out of nothing?

_____ 3. All we must really believe in Genesis 1–2 is that God somehow made the world, and that the details of these chapters are unimportant?

_____ 4. Genesis 1–2 is in direct conflict with science?

_____ 5. Scripture allows the possibility of man evolving from a lower form of life?

_____ 6. By adding up the genealogies in Genesis, we can find the date when man was created?

_____ 7. The language of Genesis 1–2 is poetic, rather than scientific?

_____ 8. Adam was originally made by God as a being who possessed eternal life?

_____ 9. The fall of man affected man's will, but not his capacity to reason?

The Creation of the World

The universe was originally formed by God's direct act, out of nothing (without use of any pre-existent material).

1. Psalm 33:6—What action caused the world to exist?

_____

_____

2. Hebrews 11:3—Of what is this present creation ("things which are seen") *not* made?

_____

_____

While those who accept the authority of the Bible commonly agree that God sovereignly made the world out of nothing, there are many different views concerning the exact meaning of the "days of creation" in Genesis 1.*

1. *View One—Short Days/Young Earth (Evening-morning regular days)*

   a. The normal meaning of the word *yom* (day) in the Bible refers to a twenty-four-hour period.

   b. The expression "morning and evening" points to exact time periods and in Genesis 1:5 effectively defines the creation days as approximating to normal days today.

   c. God is able to create in such a way as to give the appearance of age (for example, Adam was created full grown and mature when only a minute old).

   d. The context of the chapter does not force *yom* to mean anything but a day of ordinary length.

---

*Editor's note: These three examples of differing views held by Bible-believing theologians are not presented here as if to say it is unimportant as to which view you hold. The original intention of the *Westminster Confession of Faith* on the "days of creation" has been convincingly demonstrated to be that of "evening and morning" days similar to our normal days. Creation days were not identical to our non-creative providential days, but the analogy between the two points to short periods like our solar days, rather than ages of time.

e. Our one-in-seven Sabbath day falls on God's actual one-in-seven creation rest day, while looking forward to an eternal Sabbath for God's people.

2. *View Two—Long Days/Old Earth (Day-Age Theory)*

   a. *Definition:* The word for "day" is sometimes used in the Bible to indicate an age or era of time. The geological makeup of our world would seem to indicate longer periods of formation than a space of six days. The chronology of Genesis 1 is accurate and gives us the exact *order* of what God did in six consecutive periods.

   b. Genesis 2:4—How long a period of time is referred to here by the word "day" *(yom)*?

   _____

   (Does this prove that the other days the "day" encompasses are also days that encompass a number of other days, or years?)

   c. Zechariah 4:10—How is "day" *(yom)* used here?

   _____

   d. 2 Peter 3:8—What are we told about "days" from God's perspective?

   _____

   (Does the context refer to Creation? To what does this refer?)

   e. The first three "days" of creation took place before the formation of the sun and the moon, which control our normal twenty-four-hour day. *(Does this prove that sunless days must be great ages?)*

   f. The seventh day of creation marks the end of God's creative activity and is itself an eternal Sabbath rest, not a twenty-four-hour period.

3. *View Three—The Literary Framework Theory*

   a. *Definition:* This view insists that God actually formed the world out of nothing and claims to hold that Genesis is historical in some sense. However, it proposes that there is a literary rather than a scientifically technical framework to Genesis 1. The "days" are not necessarily to be viewed as either six ordinary days or eras, but rather as a semi-poetic teaching device by which God conveyed a vivid picture of His absolute power in creation.

   b. Genesis 1:1-31

      1) In verses 5, 8, 13, 19, 23, 31, what *refrain line* occurs in each case?

      _____

(Does that poetic repetition necessitate a less than literal application of the words? Compare the refrain in Psalm 136. Is that poetic repetition in any way a diminution of the literal enduring mercies of God?)

2) The perfectly balanced literary structure of the Genesis account can be seen even in the parallels between the first group of three days and the second group of three days. Complete this listing in order to see the structure:

What was made   *What was made*

Day 1 _____   Day 4 _____

Day 2 _____   Day 5 _____

Day 3 _____   Day 6 _____

How does Day 4 tie in with Day 1? _____

How does Day 5 tie in with Day 2? _____

How does Day 6 tie in with Day 3? _____

Note: Is this necessarily incompatible with a literal sequence of unfolding creative acts?

Man as Created by God

God directly formed man as a living being. Man *is* the totality of his person. He is *both* body *and* soul.

1. Genesis 2:7a—What did God use to make the body of Adam?

_____

_____

2. Genesis 2:7b—If God breathed "life" into man, could he have existed as a lower form of animal?

_____

_____

Man as originally created by God bore His image in knowledge, righteousness and holiness.

1. Genesis 1:27—How did God say He made male and female?

_____

2. Genesis 1:31—What is God's evaluation of His whole creation, including man?

   _____

   _____

3. Colossians 3:10—How is the new man described here?

   _____

   _____

4. Ephesians 4:24—What characteristics of the new man are given here?

   _____

   _____

5. James 3:9—How are men described as being made?

   _____

   _____

   Note: NKJV "similitude" is unnecessarily archaic. "Likeness" is just fine.

   Does this include even unbelievers?

   _____

   _____

Man was given dominion over the rest of creation. This is frequently called the "cultural mandate."

1. Genesis 1:28—What two basic tasks did God assign Adam? (Watch for parallel expressions.)

   _____

   _____

2. Psalm 8:6—What is man's relationship to the rest of God's creation?

   _____

   _____

3. Hebrews 2:6-8—How does this passage relate the words of Psalm 8:6 to the work of Christ?

_____

_____

The Fall of Man

Definition: Adam, as the federal head of the human race, was created without sin. Willfully disobeying God's prohibition, he brought sin's corruption into his very nature and has thus passed sin on to all his posterity.

The events in the Garden of Eden

1. The probation—Genesis 2:17—What was it?

_____

_____

Note: There is no reason to consider the tree a magical tree.

2. The serpent's lie—Genesis 3:4—What was it?

_____

_____

Note: Satan is *not* a serpent, but entered into that beast for the purpose of tempting Adam.

3. The serpent's promise—Genesis 3:5—What was it?

_____

_____

4. The separation—Genesis 3:8—How did Adam and Eve display their guilt?

_____

_____

5. The curse from God—Genesis 3:14, 16-17—How was each punished?

a. Serpent _____

b. Eve _____

c. Adam _____

The Relationship of Adam to Humanity

Romans 5:12

1. Who is the "one man"? _____

2. What did he bring into the world? _____

3. What sentence came upon all men? _____

4. What have all men also done? _____

Psalm 51:5—What does David say is true even of children?

_____

_____

Ephesians 2:1—What is the condition of man because of sin?

_____

_____

Note: Scripture distinguishes between *original sin* (the guilt of Adam, which all men share in by their very nature as his descendants) and *actual sin* (the sinful deeds or acts committed by man himself). To cease from a particular sin does not solve man's sin problem because his nature is still sinful (see Matt. 15:19; Jer. 17:9).

For Discussion

1. What reason underlies modern man's insistence on evolution?

2. Why do psychologists today often reject the biblical idea that man has a soul?

3. Why is it important to believe in a literal Adam and Eve as our first parents?

4. Why does God who is perfect and all-powerful allow sin in the world?

5. How has the Fall affected the cultural mandate? What is its relation to the Great Commission?

6 Do animals have the same rights as humans? How does the doctrine of man as "the image of God" impact this question?

Digging Deeper...

1. Thomas Boston, *Human Nature in its Fourfold State,* Banner of Truth, 506 pp. *One of the great classic works of Reformed Christian doctrine, examines man's nature as originally created, fallen, redeemed, and glorified.*

2. John C. Whitcomb and Henry M. Morris, *The Genesis Flood,* Presbyterian & Reformed, 489 pp. *A comprehensive and compelling presentation of the biblical record and its scientific implications.*

3. Douglas F. Kelly, *Creation and Change: Genesis 1.1–2.4 in the light of changing scientific paradigms,* Mentor, 272 pp. *By the professor of systematic theology at Reformed Theological Seminary, Charlotte, N.C.*

4. Henry M. Morris, *The Genesis Record,* Baker Books, 716 pp.

The Person & Work of Jesus Christ

Memorize

Colossians 2:9
For in Him dwells all the fullness of the Godhead bodily . . .

Shorter Catechism
Q 21: Who is the Redeemer of God's elect?
A: The only Redeemer of God's elect is the Lord Jesus Christ, who, being the eternal Son of God, became man, and so was, and continueth to be, God and man in two distinct natures, and one person, for ever.

Suggested Readings
Confession of Faith—Chapter 8
Reformed Presbyterian Testimony—Chapter 8

The Person of Jesus Christ

Definition: Christ is *one person* with *two natures.* He is both God and man, having a dual consciousness and a dual will. There is no fusion of His natures: For example, He continued to know all things as God; but as man (second Adam) He learned by the same processes other humans do, only without sin.

Jesus Christ is truly God.

1. Isaiah 9:6—How does Isaiah speak of Christ's divine character?

   _____

   _____

2. Jeremiah 23:6—What is Jeremiah's title for Christ?

   _____

   _____

3. John 17:10—How does Jesus state His equality with the Father?

   _____

   _____

4. Colossians 2:9—How does Paul express the deity of Jesus Christ?

_____

_____

Jesus Christ is also truly man, but without sin as the Second Adam.

1. John 4:6—What human trait did Jesus display here?

_____

_____

2. 1 John 4:2—How has Jesus come to us?

_____

_____

3. Hebrews 4:15—In what way was Jesus as a man unlike all other men?

_____

_____

4. 1 Corinthians 15:45, 47

   a. Who is referred to here as "the last Adam" (v. 45)?

   _____

   b. How is "the first man" characterized in verse 47?

   _____

   c. How is "the second man" identified in verse 47?

   _____

Jesus Christ is revealed in Scripture as existing in different conditions or states.

1. The Pre-Incarnate State

   Before His birth, Christ existed as the eternally begotten Son, the Second Person of the Trinity, equal in power and authority with the Father.

   a. Psalm 2:7—How does God refer to Jesus here?

   _____

b. John 1:1-3—What does this passage tell us about Jesus (the Word) before He came to earth in human flesh?

_____

2. The State of Humiliation

   a. The Incarnation of Christ (Jesus was supernaturally conceived by the Holy Spirit in the womb of a virgin. He humbled Himself by thus adding a human nature to His divine person.)

      1) John 1:14—What did the Word (Christ) become?

      _____

      2) Galatians 4:4—In what two ways did Christ choose to be like us?

      _____

      3) Luke 1:34-35—How did Jesus' birth differ from all other human beings?

      _____

   b. The Suffering of Christ

      1) Hebrews 5:8—What was necessary for Jesus to learn through suffering?

      _____

      2) 1 Pet. 4:1—Why did Christ suffer in the flesh?

      _____

   c. The Death of Christ

      1) Isaiah 53:12—What was the purpose of Christ's death?

      _____

      2) Galatians 3:13—How did Christ redeem us from the curse of the law?

      _____

   d. The Burial of Christ

      1) Isaiah 53:9—Where does Isaiah prophesy Christ's burial will take place?

      _____

2) Luke 23:33, 50-53—What facts are given here to show that Isaiah's prophecy is fulfilled?

_____

3. The Exaltation of Christ (See Philippians 2:5-11)

   a. The Resurrection of Christ

      1) Psalm 16:10—What is prophesied of Christ here?

_____

      2) Romans 10:9—What must be done in order to be saved?

_____

   b. The Ascension of Christ

      1) Acts 1:9—What did the disciples see happen to Christ?

_____

      2) John 20:17—What did Jesus say He was going to do?

_____

   c. The Session (seating) at God's Right Hand

     Note: Christ will be visible to us in heaven because He will have a resurrected, immortal body.

      1) 1 Peter 3:22—How does Peter describe where Christ is today?

_____

      2) Ephesians 2:6—Who also shares in Christ's exaltation to the presence of God?

_____

   d. The Return of Christ

      1) Acts 1:11—What does the angel promise the disciples?

_____

      2) 2 Cor. 5:10—What is the immediate purpose of Christ's return?

_____

Christ's Threefold Work

Christ is our *Prophet* who reveals God and His truth to us.

1. Deuteronomy 18:15—What is Moses saying here? (See Acts 3:22)

   _____

2. John 8:26-28—What does Jesus claim about His teachings?

   _____

Christ is our *Priest*, who as our Mediator both offers the sacrifice of Himself for us and makes intercession for us. Only because He is both God and man is His priestly work sufficient and able to save His people.

1. Psalm 110:4—What is prophesied of Christ here?

   _____

   _____

2. 1 Timothy 2:5—What is Christ's unique position?

   _____

   _____

3. 1 Peter 2:24—What is the nature of the sacrifice Christ offers?

   _____

   _____

4. Romans 8:34—What is Christ's work now?

   _____

   _____

Christ as our *King* rules as Head of His Church now and eternally over all present and future creation.

1. 2 Samuel 7:12-13—What does David desire here for Solomon that is fulfilled only in Christ?

   _____

   _____

2. John 18:36-37—How does Jesus describe His Kingdom?

_____

_____

3. Ephesians 1:22—What is Christ's authority as Mediator for the Church?

_____

_____

For Discussion

1. Why is it important to believe that Christ was both God and man?

2. Name some groups that deny either His humanity or His divinity.

3. Why do some deny the virgin birth yet still claim Christ is the Son of God?

4. Why does Scripture call Christ the "last Adam"?

5. How does Roman Catholicism view the birth of Christ?

6. Does Christ have a visible body today?

Digging Deeper...

1. Benjamin B. Warfield, *The Person and Work of Christ,* Presbyterian & Reformed, 575 pp. *A collection of the writings of the late Princeton theologian with three sermons appended.*

2. Frederick S. Leahy, *The Cross He Bore,* Banner of Truth, 82 pp. *Deeply moving meditations on the sufferings of the Redeemer by the principal of the Reformed Theological College, Belfast.*

3. Frederick S. Leahy, *The Victory of the Lamb,* Banner of Truth, 126 pp. *More stirring reflections of Christ's triumph over sin, death, and Satan.*

The Holy Spirit

Memorize

2 Thessalonians 2:13
But we are bound to give thanks to God always for you, brethren beloved by the Lord, because God from the beginning chose you for salvation through sanctification by the Spirit and belief in the truth.

Shorter Catechism
Q 30: How doth the Spirit apply to us the redemption purchased by Christ?
A: The Spirit applieth to us the redemption purchased by Christ, by working faith in us, and thereby uniting us to Christ in our effectual calling.

Suggested Reading
Reformed Presbyterian Testimony—Chapter 2

The Person of the Holy Spirit

He is revealed to us in Scripture as possessing the attributes of personality. He is *not* merely an abstract force and should *not* be addressed as "it."

1.   Ephesians 4:30—What personal emotion of the Spirit is noted here?

_____

2.   Luke 12:12—What personal activity of the Spirit is noted here?

_____

The Spirit is revealed to us as the third Person of the Trinity equal in substance, power, and authority with the Father and the Son.

1.   Romans 8:9—What two titles are given to the Spirit here?

_____

2.   Matthew 28:19—(Review the statements in Lesson 2 concerning this passage and the general subject of the Trinity.) Who are the three distinct Persons under whose authority baptism is to be administered?

_____

The Work of the Holy Spirit

The Spirit works in behalf of all creation. (This is often referred to as the realm of Common Grace.)

In the exercise below indicate the passages from the list of Scripture passages below that best describe the particular activity of the Spirit mentioned in the left-hand column:

The Spirit acts as: *Passage:*

1. the Agent of creation   _____

2. the Giver of life   _____

3. the Giver of reason   _____

4. the Giver of artistic ability   _____

5. the Giver of conscience and
    common social morality   _____

6. the Giver of providential blessings   _____

> *Passages:*
> Rom. 2:14-15   Gen. 1:2   Ps. 145:9
> Ex. 31:2-3, 5   Job 33:4   Job 32:8

The Spirit also works specifically in behalf of God's elect. (This is commonly called the realm of Special or Saving Grace.)

Complete the exercise as previously. Use the Scripture passages on the next page.

The Spirit acts for God's people as: *Passage:*

1. the Agent of the inspiration of
    Scripture   _____

2. the Applier of the benefits of Christ's death and resurrection who:

    a. convicts of sin   _____

    b. regenerates the heart   _____

    c. enlightens the mind   _____

    d. comforts or defends   _____

    e. sanctifies the life   _____

f.   assures of salvation _____

g.   makes intercession _____

h.   gives us resurrection bodies _____

3.   the Granter of the gifts for office in the church _____

> *Passages:*
> John 16:13   John 16:8   1 Cor. 12:1-7   John 3:5, 8   Rom. 8:11
> John 14:16   2 Pet. 1:21   2 Thess. 2:13   1 John 3:24   Rom. 8:26

The Spirit in the Life of the Believer

All believers are indwelt by the Holy Spirit at all times.

1.   Romans 8:9—What must an individual have to be a Christian?

_____

2.   Romans 8:14—Who are the sons of God?

_____

3.   1 Corinthians 3:16—What is the relationship of the Spirit to all believers?

_____

The Holy Spirit enters the believer's life at the time of his rebirth. This is also called the "baptism" of the Spirit, but does no6t refer to any "second blessing" occurring after conversion.

1.   John 3:3, 8—What two expressions are used in these verses to refer to salvation?

_____

2.   Matthew 3:11—What is the nature of Jesus' baptism as opposed to John's?

_____

Note: The outward sacrament of baptism is a sign and seal of the inward work of the baptism of the Spirit (i.e. regeneration received by faith).

3.   Acts 19:2-6—Why had this group not received the Holy Spirit?

_____

4. Galatians 3:2-3—How and when did the believers in Galatia receive the Spirit?

The believer is always to seek to be filled with the Holy Spirit for powerful service and growth in grace, but this fullness can be diminished by the believer's neglect and sins. The fullness of the Holy Spirit should be the normal condition of every believer.

1. Acts 9:17—What was Christ's plan for Paul? (See Acts 13:9)

2. Ephesians 5:18—What positive command is given to all believers?

3. 1 Thessalonians 5:19—What are believers to avoid?

Note: The fact that we are commanded to seek this filling implies that there will be times when we have less of the power of the Spirit in our lives. This does not imply, however, that at any time the believer loses the indwelling presence of the Spirit in his life as the guarantor of his salvation.

For Discussion

1. How does the Holy Spirit lead believers today? Does He reveal truth apart from Scripture?

2. What is the unpardonable sin? (See Mark 3:29; Hebrews 6:1-8.)

3. How does Pentecostalism view the work of the Spirit?

Digging Deeper...

1. Sinclair B. Ferguson, *The Holy Spirit,* Banner of Truth, 240 pp. *Part of the Contours of Christian Philosophy Series.*

2. Victor Budgen, *The Charismatics and the Word of God,* Evangelical Press, 287 pp. *A biblical and historical perspective on the charismatic movement.*

3. John Owen, *A Discourse on the Holy Spirit,* Banner of Truth, 208 pp. *Abridged version of this classic specimen of Puritan scholarship focusing on the third Person of the Trinity in His nature and operations.*

Plan of Salvation (Part 1)

> **Memorize**
>
> Ephesians 2:8-10
> *For by grace you have been saved through faith, and that not of yourselves; it is the gift of God, not of works, lest anyone should boast. For we are His work-manship, created in Christ Jesus for good works, which God prepared before-hand that we should walk in them.*
>
> Shorter Catechism
> *Q 30: How doth the Spirit apply to us the redemption purchased by Christ?*
> *A: The Spirit applieth to us the redemption purchased by Christ, by working faith in us, and thereby uniting us to Christ in our effectual calling.*

Suggested Readings
Confession of Faith—Chapters 9, 14, 16
Reformed Presbyterian Testimony—Chapters 9, 14, 16

Total Depravity

Definition: Man's nature is sinful throughout; he is totally unable to save himself from the consequences of his own sin.

Sin defiles man's total personality.

1. Romans 8:7-8—What is the fleshly mind unable to do?

    _____

2. Mark 7:21-23—From what aspect of man's being do the sins listed here proceed?

    _____

3. John 3:19—What is the relation of non-Christians to sin (darkness)?

    _____

Sin enslaves man.

1. Romans 6:20—What are unbelievers called here?

    _____

2. Acts 26:18—Under whose power are unbelievers?

_____

Sin reigns over all men.

1. 1 John 5:19—What is said about the whole world here?

_____

2. Ecclesiastes 7:20—What kind of man does *not* exist?

_____

3. Romans 3:9-12—Name three things here that a "natural man" does not do.

_____

Sinners have neither the desire nor the ability to be saved.

1. Jeremiah 13:23—What do the Ethiopian and the leopard tell us about man's ability to do good?

_____

2. John 6:44—What must first happen in order for a person to come to Christ?

_____

3. John 6:65—What expression is used here to show what must happen before man can come to Christ?

_____

Unconditional Election

Definition: In eternity God chose to save some and reject others according to His sovereign good pleasure. Election rests solely on grace, not foreseen merit in those elected.

God selects some and rejects others.

1. Romans 8:28—Those who love God are also stated to be those who are:

_____

2. Colossians 3:12—Christians are referred to here as the:

_____

3. Matthew 22:14—Many are called but:

_____

God's electing act took place in eternity.

1. Ephesians 1:4—When are we chosen?

_____

2. Revelations 17:8—What does this verse imply about the time when *believers'* names are recorded in the book of life?

_____

God's choice of His people does not rest upon foreseen merit in those whom He elects.

1. Romans 9:11-13

   a. When did God choose Jacob over Esau?

   _____

   b. Why was this choice made?

   _____

2. Romans 9:16

   a. What two actions do not bring man salvation?

   _____

   b. What is the basis of salvation?

   _____

Good works are the result and proof of election, not the grounds for it.

Ephesians 2:10

1. To what purpose are we "created in Christ Jesus"?

_____

2. What relationship have our works to God's plan?

_____

Even faith is a result of God's electing grace, not the cause of it.

1. Ephesians 2:8-9—State both what faith is not, and what faith is.

    _____

2. Acts 18:27—Through what means are we enabled to believe?

    _____

God alone determines those to whom He will give the gift of salvation.

1. Exodus 33:19—What words does God use here to express His sovereignty in election?

    _____

2. Romans 9:18—Upon whom does God have mercy?

    _____

3. Ephesians 1:5—On what basis are we predestined to adoption through Christ?

    _____

Exercise:

Answer these common objections in your own words. Use Scripture to back your answers.

1. It is unfair for God to choose some and reject others.

    _____

    _____

2. If God does all the work in salvation, we don't have to do anything.

    _____

    _____

3. Predestination amounts to fatalism and makes machines out of us.

    _____

    _____

For Discussion

1. If man is totally depraved, how can the unregenerate person do worthwhile things? (See Matthew 7:11.)

2. What is involved in God's rejecting some and electing others? What is meant by hardening in Romans 9:18?

Digging Deeper...

1. John Murray, *Redemption Accomplished and Applied,* Eerdmans, 181 pp. *A wonderfully insightful examination of the free and sovereign love of God as the source of salvation.*

2. David N. Steele and Curtis C. Thomas, *The Five Points of Calvinism,* Presbyterian & Reformed, 91 pp. *A plain and lucid presentation of the sovereignty of God in salvation.*

3. Cesar Malan, *The Church is Mine,* Evangelical Press, 144 pp. *A marvelous explanation of Christ's atonement for the sin of sinners, which is how He makes the Church His own.*

Plan of Salvation (Part 2)

Memorize

Ephesians 2:8-10

For by grace you have been saved through faith, and that not of yourselves; it is the gift of God, not of works, lest anyone should boast. For we are His workmanship, created in Christ Jesus for good works, which God prepared beforehand that we should walk in them.

Shorter Catechism

Q 30: How doth the Spirit apply to us the redemption purchased by Christ?
A: The Spirit applieth to us the redemption purchased by Christ, by working faith in us, and thereby uniting us to Christ in our effectual calling.

Suggested Readings—See previous lesson.

Limited Atonement

Definition: The death of Christ secures complete salvation for all the elect people of God, but not all of mankind. This view is also called the particular or definite atonement. Arminians, who reject the Reformed view that limits the extent of the atonement to the elect, do not realize that they have falsely limited the power of the atonement, in that if Christ dies for all and all are not saved, then men can thwart the very power and purpose of God.

Christ's death was a substitutionary act.

1. 1 Peter 2:24a—What did Christ do for us?

    _____

2. Mark 10:45—Jesus gave His life as a:

    _____

3. Isaiah 53:6—What did the Lord lay upon Christ?

    _____

Christ's death guarantees complete salvation for all He planned to save. He does not merely make it possible for people to choose or reject salvation on their own.

1. Titus 2:14—Why does Christ "give" Himself?

    _____

39

2. Romans 5: 10—What is promised us because of Christ's death?

    _____

3. Hebrews 9:12—What kind of redemption is provided by Christ's death?

    _____

Christ's atoning death applies specifically to the elect.

1. Matthew 1:21—Whom does Christ save? _____

2. John 10:24-28—To whom does Christ give eternal life? _____

3. Matthew 20:28—For whom is Christ the ransom? _____

4. Acts 20:28—For whom is Christ's blood shed? _____

5. Hebrews 9:15—Who receives the eternal inheritance through Christ's death?

    _____

Irresistible Grace

Definition: The special working of the Holy Spirit in the life of one of the elect whereby he is given the eyes of faith and his nature is so changed that he freely accepts Christ as He is offered in the gospel.

The free offer of the gospel is to be extended to all men: We cannot determine who are the elect.

1. Matthew 28:19—To whom should the gospel be preached?

    _____

2. Revelation 14:6—To whom will the gospel be preached?

    _____

There will be those who do not respond in faith to the gospel offer.

1. Mark 8:18—How does Jesus describe these unbelievers?

    _____

2. 1 Corinthians 1:23—What is the reaction of unsaved men to the gospel?

    _____

In order for a man who is dead in sin to respond to the gospel, the Holy Spirit must first work in his heart, through the Word. Regeneration precedes faith and conversion.

1. Titus 3:5—What two "r's" is the Spirit responsible for?

   _____

2. 1 Corinthians 2:12—Why have we received the Spirit which is from God?

   _____

3. 2 Corinthians 5:17—How are believers described here?

   _____

4. Acts 16:14—What did God do for Lydia?

   _____

5. 1 Peter 1:23—What is the means of our new birth?

   _____

The special inward call of the Holy Spirit always results in the conversion of those to whom it is made.

1. Romans 8:30—After God's people are called, what else does He do for them?

   _____

2. 1 Peter 2:9—God has called us from what into what?

   _____

Perseverance of the Saints

Definition: All God's elect have secured eternal salvation through faith in Christ, and shall be glorified by Him at the Last Day.

The new life given to believers is eternal, not temporary or subject to loss.

1. Jeremiah 32:40

   a. What kind of covenant does God make with His elect?

   _____

   b. What does He keep us from doing?

   _____

2. John 5:24

    a. What *immediate* possession belongs to the one who hears and believes?

    _____

    b. What does he escape?

    _____

Our security (perseverance) rests on God's work, not our own merits.

1. John 6:35-40

    a. What will Jesus not do to the one who comes to Him? (v. 37)

    _____

    b. What is the Father's will concerning the believer's security? (v. 39)

    _____

    c. What are believers promised at the end of the world? (v. 40)

    _____

2. John 10:27-30

    a. What will believers never do?

    _____

    b. What can no one do to them?

    _____

3. Romans 8:39—From what can believers never be separated?

    _____

Although our eternal security does not rest upon our good works, our works are one proof that we are eternally saved.

1. Matthew 7:20—How does Jesus say believers can be singled out?

    _____

2. John 14:21—Who truly loves Christ?

    _____

There will be certain individuals who think they are Christians who are not actually saved.

1. Matthew 7:21-23—Whom does Jesus say will enter heaven? (v. 21)

   _____

   What will Jesus say to those who say they are Christians, engage in religious activity, but actually never trust Christ for their salvation?

   _____

2. John 15:6—Who are those who are cast out?

   _____

FOR FURTHER STUDY

How do you explain these verses if you accept the doctrine of the limited atonement?

The "all" passages. Read 1 Timothy 2:3-6; Hebrews 2:9.

1. The context and sense of a passage when compared also with the other passages of Scripture on the same subject indicate to us whether "all" means in general or every single individual.

2. What does "all" mean in Matthew 10:22?

   _____

3. Does Paul mean every last Jew in Acts 26:4?

   _____

4. Romans 3:9-10—Does "all" mean without exception?

   _____

5. Does the context of Hebrews 2:9-16 limit the "every man" of verse 9?

   _____

6. 1 Timothy 2:4—In the light of the rest of Scripture on this subject does "all" mean that God will have every last individual to be saved? What does "will have" mean?

   _____

FOR FURTHER STUDY
(continued)

The "world" passages. Read John 1:29; 3:16.

1. What was the common Jewish idea about what nations would be saved?

   _____

2. In Luke 2:1, does the expression "whole world" mean down to the last individual?

   _____

3. In John 12:19, does "the world" mean every last person?

   _____

4. How has the whole world benefited from Christ's death?

   _____

5. In John 1:29 and 3:16, does the context then indicate that "the world" means every last individual upon the surface of the earth?

   _____

God's "will" to save us. Read 2 Peter 3:9.

1. What do we mean by the revealed and secret (decreed) will of God?

   _____

2. If men do go to hell, is God limited in His power?

   _____

3. Is the word "will" in 2 Peter 3:9 a reference to God's sovereign purpose or His general revealed plan for mankind?

   _____

What are the three elements necessary for assurance of salvation (1 John 3:23-24)?

1. _____

2. _____

3. _____

For Discussion

1. Why is it important to our sanctification to see that regeneration comes before faith and conversion?

2. How can Hebrews 6:4-6 be explained if we accept the doctrine of eternal security?

3. Is it possible for an individual to lose the assurance (subjective) of his salvation without losing his salvation itself?

Digging Deeper...

1. John Murray, *Redemption Accomplished and Applied,* Eerdmans, 181 pp. *A wonderfully insightful examination of the free and sovereign love of God as the source of salvation.*

2. David N. Steele and Curtis C. Thomas, *The Five Points of Calvinism,* Presbyterian & Reformed, 91 pp. *A plain and lucid presentation of the sovereignty of God in salvation.*

3. Cesar Malan, *The Church is Mine,* Evangelical Press, 144 pp. *A marvelous explanation of Christ's atonement for the sin of sinners, which is how He makes the Church His own.*

The Christian Life (Part 1)

Memorize

Matthew 22:37-39
Jesus said to him, "'You shall love the Lord your God with all your heart, with all your soul, and with all your mind.' This is the first and great commandment. And the second is like it: 'You shall love your neighbor as yourself.'"

Romans 3:24
Being justified freely by His grace through the redemption that is in Christ Jesus.

Shorter Catechism
Q. 39: What is the duty which God requireth of man?
A: The duty which God requireth of man, is obedience to his revealed will.

Q. 40: What did God at first reveal to man for the rule of his obedience?
A: The rule which God at first revealed to man for his obedience, was the moral law.

Q. 41: Where is the moral law summarily comprehended?
A: The moral law is summarily comprehended in the ten commandments.

Q. 42: What is the sum of the ten commandments?
A: The sum of the ten commandments is, to love the Lord our God, with all our heart, with all our soul, with all our strength, and with all our mind; and our neighbor as ourselves.

Suggested Readings
Confession of Faith—Chapters 19–20
Reformed Presbyterian Testimony—Chapters 19–20

The Christian and the Moral Law

The Law was given to display God's holiness, and to bring man under conviction of sin as he views himself in the light of God's righteous demands.

1. Romans 7:12—How is God's Law described?

2. Romans 3:20—What does Paul say the Law gives us?

_____

3. Galatians 3:24—What does the Law as "schoolmaster" do?

_____

A man is unable to earn his salvation by keeping the Law perfectly because of his sinful nature.

1. James 2:10—What does James warn men of here?

_____

2. Romans 3:20—What cannot be gained by obedience to the Law?

_____

3. Romans 3:24—What is the only means of justification?

_____

4. Romans 6:14-15—What is not the believer's condition? What is his condition?

_____

Note: When Paul states that the believer is no longer under the Law but under grace, he does not mean that the believer has no responsibility to keep the Law. What he is stating is that the believer's ground of salvation is not works (carrying out the Law), but faith in the righteousness of Christ as that gift of God's grace which justifies him in God's sight. The believer is now called to keep God's Law out of gratitude for his salvation.

The Moral Law, however, is to be obeyed by believers as the evidence and fruit of salvation, not the means of it.

1. Romans 3:31—What effect does Paul say that faith-righteousness has upon our relationship to the Law?

_____

2. Ephesians 2:8-10—What is the result of our being saved by grace through faith?

_____

3. 1 John 2:3—How can we tell if we are true believers?

_____

The Moral Law, which is summarized in the Ten Commandments, is the standard for believers' conduct in every age.

1. Exodus 20:1-17—Using the *Shorter Catechism* (Questions 45-81) as an aid, give a brief statement in your own words that summarizes the duties required in each specific commandment. State both the positive and negative aspects of each commandment.

   Our Duty to God

   I. _____

   II. _____

   III. _____

   IV. _____

   Our Duty to Fellow Men

   V. _____

   VI. _____

   VII. _____

   VIII. _____

   IX. _____

   X. _____

2. Matthew 22:34-40—How does Jesus summarize the whole Moral Law?

   _____

   What does He mean by saying that on these two commands "hangs all the law and the prophets"?

   _____

The Christian is morally responsible for the effect of his actions upon fellow believers.

1. Romans 14:13–15:1-2

   a. 14:13—What must we avoid?

   _____

   What is a stumbling block?

   _____

b.   14:14—What does Paul mean here?

_____

c.   14:15—What does it mean to be grieved?

_____

What is said of those who neglect their brother's welfare?

_____

d.   15:1-2—What is the job of the stronger brother?

_____

2.   1 Corinthians 8:9-13

a.   v. 12—What have we done if we wound the weak conscience of a brother?

_____

b.   v. 13—What principle is Paul stating here?

_____

For Discussion

1. Evaluate contemporary morality. What are its strong and weak points?

2. Define what you mean by individual Christian liberty. How is it to be used?

3. What is meant by the "corporate testimony" of the church? How is it to be used?

4. Discuss to what extent the church may go in requiring members to refrain from actions not per se forbidden in Scripture. Relate this discussion to Acts 15 and the letter sent out to the Early Church from the Council at Jerusalem.

5. What procedure should a Christian use in determining whether a certain action is sinful for him? List the questions he must face.

6. What do you think of the statement, "If it's questionable, it's wrong"?

Digging Deeper...

1. Sinclair B. Ferguson, _The Christian Life, A Doctrinal Introduction,_ Banner of Truth, 201 pp. _Helpful exposition on such themes as grace, faith, repentance, new birth and assurance._

2. J. C. Ryle, _Holiness,_ Charles Nolan, 440 pp. _A true classic on the new life that believers are called and equipped to live by the grace of God in Christ._

3. Francis A. Schaeffer, _True Spirituality,_ Tyndale, 180 pp. _Insightful treatment of the causes and cures of spiritual bondage._

The Christian Life (Part 2)

Memorize

2 Corinthians 5:17
Therefore, if anyone is in Christ, he is a new creation; old things have passed away; behold, all things have become new.

1 John 1:9
If we confess our sins, He is faithful and just to forgive us our sins and to cleanse us from all unrighteousness.

Shorter Catechism
Q 82: Is any man able perfectly to keep the commandments of God?
A: No mere man since the fall is able in this life perfectly to keep the commandments of God, but doth daily break them in thought, word, and deed.

Q 85: What doth God require of us, that we may escape his wrath and curse, due to us for sin?
A: To escape the wrath and curse of God, due to us for sin, God requireth of us faith in Jesus Christ, repentance unto life, with the diligent use of all the outward means whereby Christ communicateth to us the benefits of redemption.

Suggested Readings
Confession of Faith—Chapters 8 and 15
Reformed Presbyterian Testimony—Chapters 8 and 15

The Christian and Indwelling Sin

When a person is regenerated by the Holy Spirit he receives a new nature.

1. 2 Corinthians 5:17—What does Paul say is the result of being "in Christ"?

   _____

   _____

2. Ezekiel 36:26—What does God promise to do in salvation?

   _____

The old nature is destroyed when a person is regenerated.

1. Romans 6:6—What does Paul say has already happened to the old man?

   _____

2. Colossians 3:9-10—What does Paul say has already taken place that should encourage us to avoid sinning?

   _____

Because sin is no longer the nature of the Christian, he now is able to have victory over sin.

1. Romans 6:11-12—What is required of us here?

   _____

2. Colossians 3:1-10—What are the basic duties of the one who has put on the new man?

   _____

3. 1 John 3:6-9—Why does John say the Christian cannot commit sin?

   _____

   Note: To commit "sin" means to make sin one's unrepentant lifestyle and continued practice.

In this life, however, the believer is not removed from all possibility of falling into sin.

1. 1 John 1:8—What does John say about believers here?

   _____

   Does he refer to a present or past condition?

   _____

2. Romans 7:19-23

   a. v. 19—What is Paul's problem?

      _____

   b. v. 20—How does he explain what happens?

      _____

c. v. 21—What is his conclusion?

_____

d. v. 22—Is this a description of a believer or an unbeliever?

_____

e. v. 23—What wars against the new nature that Paul has as a believer?

_____

Note: The believer must continually wage war against "the law of sin" that abides within him. This law of sin, however, can be conquered and subdued through Christ, because it is not an actual part of the believer's own nature, but an outside force at war against him.

The Christian has victory over sin by claiming Christ's righteousness through faith.

1. 1 John 2:1—What does John promise the believer when he sins?

_____

2. 1 John 1:7—What is the means of cleansing?

_____

3. 1 John 1:9—How may we obtain God's forgiveness?

_____

4. 1 Corinthians 10:13—What lessons are believers to learn from this verse?

_____

5. Galatians 2:20-21—How does Paul explain the new righteousness in his life?

_____

For Discussion

1. What is the work of the Holy Spirit in the sanctification of the believer? How does God's sovereignty relate to our responsibility to live according to Christ's commands (see *Larger Catechism,* Questions 75-77)?

2. If Christians are never totally free from sin in this life, why does Jesus tell us to "be perfect even as your Father which is in heaven is perfect"? What do you think about Christians who claim to be "totally sanctified"?

3. How do we know we have deliverance from a certain sin? Is deliverance always instantaneous or can it be gradual? Can a Christian who has been delivered from a certain sin fall back into it?

4. How long may a person continue in a certain sin and still believe himself to be a Christian?

5. What are the signs of true repentance? (See 2 Cor. 7:8-11)

6. How can I know if I have made a genuine confession and been forgiven?

7. If our bodies (our total personalities) are God's temples, what does He require of us regarding their care?

Digging Deeper...

1. Sinclair B. Ferguson, *The Christian Life, A Doctrinal Introduction,* Banner of Truth, 201 pp. *Helpful exposition on such themes as grace, faith, repentance, new birth and assurance.*

2. J. C. Ryle, *Holiness,* Charles Nolan, 440 pp. *A true classic on the new life that believers are called and equipped to live by the grace of God in Christ.*

3. Francis A. Schaeffer, *True Spirituality,* Tyndale, 180 pp. *Insightful treatment of the causes and cures of spiritual bondage.*

The Church

Memorize

1 Peter 2:9
Then the Lord knows how to deliver the godly out of temptations and to reserve the unjust under punishment for the day of judgment.

Suggested Readings
Confession of Faith—Chapter 25
Reformed Presbyterian Testimony—Chapter 25

The Church Described

Various titles ascribed to her by Scripture (fill them in).

1. _____ Acts 20:28

2. _____ Ephesians 1:23

3. _____ Psalm 132:13

4. _____ 1 Peter 2:5

5. _____ Revelation 21:2

The Nature of the Church

1.	*militant* (on earth)	*triumphant* (in heaven)
2.	*visible* (those who claim to belong to the church organization)	*invisible* (all true believers)
3.	*organization* (denominational structure)	*organism* (the body of Christ)

Note: There is one true Church in mystical union with Christ, but its organization presently includes various denominations.

The Attributes of the Church (internal character)

1. Unity

    a. John 10:16—What does Jesus promise will happen to Jewish and Gentile believers?

    _____

    b. John 17:21—What does Jesus pray for here?

    _____

    c. Ephesians 4:4-6—List the seven "ones" given here.

    _____

    _____

2. Holiness

    a. Exodus 19:6—What are believers to form?

    _____

    b. 1 Peter 2:9—What four descriptions are given of the Church here?

    _____

3. Catholicity (universality)

    a. Psalm 2:8—What does God promise to Christ?

    _____

    b. Revelation 7:9—Where do the group of believers described here come from?

    _____

The Marks of the Church (external characteristics)

1. True preaching

    a. Titus 2:1—What must the Church do?

    _____

    b. 2 Timothy 2:15—What is the task of the ministry?

    _____

2. Right administration of sacraments

    a. Matthew 28:19—How are Christians to be baptized?

    _____

    b. 1 Corinthians 11:28-30—What must a man do before receiving communion?

    _____

    c. 1 Corinthians 5:11—What responsibility does the Church in her sacraments have toward professing Christians who are profane of life?

    _____

3. Proper discipline

    a. 1 Corinthians 5:13—What has to be done with an unrepentant Christian?

    _____

    b. Matthew 18:15-17—What are the three steps in dealing with a sinning brother?

    _____

The Government of the Church

Christ is the Sovereign Ruler of the Church.

1. Ephesians 1:22-23—How is Christ described here in relation to His Church?

    _____

2. John 15:5—How is Christ's relationship to His Church stressed here?

    _____

Christ rules today through the ordained officers of His Church.

1. The elders

    a. The term "elder" is synonymous with "bishop."

        Titus 1:5-7—What office is referred to in verse 5?

        _____

        What is this same man called in verse 7?

        _____

b. Titus 1:5—In each congregation there is to be more than one elder.

Acts 20:17—Who does Paul send for?

_____

Acts 14:23—What was done?

_____

c. 1 Timothy 5:17—There are two functions of elders: ruling and teaching.

How does Paul describe the two forms of eldership in 1 Timothy 5:17?

_____

d. The eldership is the highest ordained office to supervise the spiritual welfare of the church.

1 Peter 5:1-2—How does Peter tell elders to oversee their flock (congregation)?

_____

1 Timothy 3:2-7—List the sixteen qualifications of an elder. Indicate whether these qualifications are personal, social, or official.

Note: Social refers to those qualifications that have to do with an individual's relationship to others; *official* refers to those qualifications that are required specifically of one who holds the office of elder.

_____

_____

_____

_____

_____

2. The deacons

a. Acts 6:1-6—Their principal duty is to supervise the physical welfare of the church as a spiritual service.

Describe the duties of the deacons mentioned here.

_____

b. Their office is an ordained office. What does Acts 6:6 indicate about the deacon's authority?

_____

c. 1 Timothy 3:8-10, 12—List the nine qualifications for a deacon. Indicate which of these are personal, social, or official.

_____

_____

_____

_____

The biblical pattern of church government is the system of higher (broader) and lower (local) courts known as presbyterianism (see diagram, p. 60). Acts 15 provides a model of presbyterianism at work. From your study of this chapter, answer the following questions:

1. What was the issue at stake?

_____

2. Who were the opposing "parties"?

_____

3. How was the dispute to be settled?

_____

4. Who had the final voice in settling this matter of doctrinal difference?

_____

5. How was the decision passed on to the whole Church?

_____

6. What principles of presbyterian government are evident in this chapter?

_____

The way presbyterian denominations have developed in America is outlined by the historical chart at the end of this lesson.

For Discussion

1. What is the Roman Catholic view of the true Church?

2. When does a denomination cease to be part of the true Church?

3. Why do denominations exist?

4. Name and explain the other two common forms of church government besides presbyterianism.

5. What is church discipline? How should it be used?

6. What is wrong with today's ecumenical movement?

Digging deeper...

1. R. B. Kuiper, *The Glorious Body of Christ,* Banner of Truth, 367 pp. *A comprehensive overview of the Bible's teaching about the Church of Jesus Christ.*

2. B. K. Kuiper, *The Church in History,* Eerdmans, 399 pp. *Designed as a textbook for Christian schools and home educators, this wonderful book presents a thumbnail sketch of church history with illustrations and interesting narrative.*

3. Various contributors, *Unto Every Good Work: A Manual for Elders,* Crown & Covenant, 129 pp. *A training manual for those aspiring to the office of elder.*

The duties and limitations of each court are outlined in the *Book of Church Government* of the Reformed Presbyterian Church of North America. The basic principle of presbyterianism is that each congregation has a full and equal voice in the government of the church through its elected representatives.

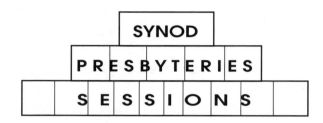

The Synod
Each minister and at least one ruling elder from each congregation compose the membership of Synod. This court meets annually to oversee the work of the whole church and to settle questions, particularly doctrinal matters, not able to be handled by the presbytery.

The Presbytery
The presbytery consists of the congregations in any one given geographical area. Its membership includes all the ministers within its bounds and at least one ruling elder from each congregation. Problems that arise in the congregations can be sent to this higher court for settlement. (See Acts 15 for an example of the presbytery at work.)

The Session
Each congregation elects its own session with a teaching elder and one or more ruling elders as the other members. They govern the local congregation.

Note: In larger denominations it is common to have a representative body in the higher courts rather than all ministers and an elder delegate from each congregation. This is frequently necessary because of the unwieldy size courts could become.

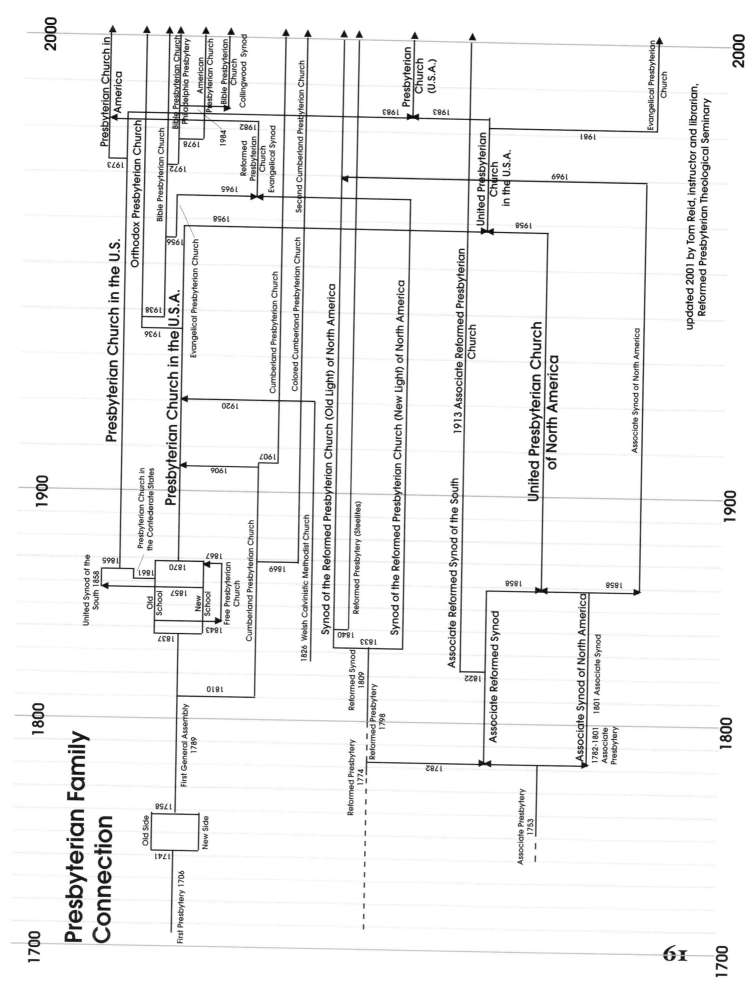

Presbyterian Family Connection

updated 2001 by Tom Reid, instructor and librarian, Reformed Presbyterian Theological Seminary

The Sacraments (Part 1)

Memorize

Shorter Catechism

Q. 92: What is a Sacrament?
A: A Sacrament is a holy ordinance instituted by Christ; wherein, by sensible signs, Christ and the benefits of the new covenant are represented, sealed, and applied to believers.

Q. 94: What is Baptism?
A: Baptism is a Sacrament, wherein the washing with water, in the name of the Father, and of the Son, and of the Holy Ghost, doth signify and seal our ingrafting into Christ, and partaking of the benefits of the covenant of grace, and our engagement to be the Lord's.

Larger Catechism

Q. 167: How is our Baptism to be improved by us?
A: The needful but much neglected duty of improving our Baptism, is to be performed by us all our life long, especially in the time of temptation, and when we are present at the administration of it to others, by serious and thankful consideration of the nature of it, and of the ends for which Christ instituted it, the privileges and benefits conferred and sealed thereby, and our solemn vow made therein; by being humbled for our sinful defilement, our falling short of, and walking contrary to, the grace of the Baptism and our engagements; by growing up to assurance of pardon of sin, and of all other blessings sealed to us in that Sacrament; by drawing strength from the death and resurrection of Christ, into whom we are baptized, for the mortifying of sin, and quickening of grace; and by endeavoring to live by faith, to have our conversation in holiness and righteousness, as those that have therein given up their names to Christ; and to walk in brotherly love, as being baptized by the same Spirit into one body.

Suggested Readings
Confession of Faith—Chapters 27–28
Reformed Presbyterian Testimony—Chapters 27–28

How Do You Understand Baptism?

Do You Think That:

_____ 1. Because a person is baptized he is therefore saved?

————— 2. An unbaptized person cannot go to heaven?

————— 3. Baptism has no meaning for a person unless he can remember when it took place?

————— 4. When a child is baptized, the child receives real benefits?

————— 5. Children must reach the "age of accountability" before they can become Christians?

————— 6. A baptized person is not a member of the Church until he or she makes a public profession of his or her faith?

————— 7. When a person changes denominations, he should always be rebaptized?

Baptism

Jesus initiated it for His Church in all ages.

1. Matthew 28:19—What is involved in the Great Commission besides preaching the gospel?

   _____

2. Acts 2:38—What two actions does Peter say are necessary before an adult can say he is a Christian?

   _____

Baptism is a sign and seal of the inward work of the Holy Spirit.

1. Three common views concerning baptism:

   a. *Automatic Grace (Roman Catholic & Lutheran View)*
   A supernatural cleansing from original sin is guaranteed if properly administered.

   b. *A Testimony Only (Zwinglian View)*
   A public, formal symbol of our inward washing by the Holy Spirit, reserved for adults who profess Christ.

   c. *A Means of Grace through Faith (Reformed)*
   A sign and seal of inclusion in the covenant of grace to be given to believers and their children.

2. Children of believers are in the covenant and should receive the sign of the covenant. The church that reserves baptism only for adults still does not avoid the problem of administering baptism to those who are not believers. It is all too easy for an adult to pretend to have faith and then be baptized. The duty of the church is to give baptism to those who profess to belong to the covenant *and to their children* because Scripture assures us they too are under that covenant. This does not mean that every infant who receives baptism is automatically saved, anymore than it means that every adult who receives baptism is automatically saved.

The *time* of baptism is not the significant factor here. What is important in every baptism is that what it signifies and seals becomes effective when received *by faith*. A child's baptism as a child of the covenant becomes fully effective when he responds to the gospel. He is to be taught early the plan of salvation by his parents and encouraged to trust Christ as his only hope of salvation, that his baptism be not in vain.

3. Baptism has a double significance when properly administered and received.

    a. Acts 2:38—What does baptism signify here?

    _____

    b. Galatians 3:27—What does baptism signify here?

    _____

The mode (immersion, pouring, sprinkling) in which the baptismal water is administered is of little significance to the validity of the baptism. The New Testament does not clearly insist on one mode above another.

1. Acts 22:16—What must occur inwardly for the promise of baptism to be fulfilled?

    _____

2. Hebrews 9:10, 13-22—What adjective is used here with the word "baptisms"? (Greek word *baptizo,* Heb. 9:10)

    _____

    How many times does the word "sprinklings" (KJV) occur in these verses?

    _____

    Note: In Hebrews 9:10, we have the expression "diverse baptisms." According to Prof. John Murray, "This reference must surely include the lustrations expressly referred to in the succeeding verses." Hence, "a lustratory rite performed by sprinkling can be called a baptism . . . . Baptism symbolizes, represents, and seals the application to us of the blood of Christ for the removal of the guilt of sin. The figure used in the New Testament for this application of the blood of Christ is that of sprinkling (Heb. 9:13-14, 22; 10:22; 12:24; 1 Pet. 1:2). It would be strange if the baptism with water which represents the sprinkling of the blood of Christ could not properly and most significantly be performed by sprinkling" (*Christian Baptism*, p. 24).

3. Acts 8:38—How does this verse prove "too much" if the reference is said to be an argument in favor of total immersion?

    _____

The normal pattern in Scripture is for adult believers (not previously baptized) to be baptized at the same time that they make public professions of faith.

1. Luke 23:39-43—Why is this event a departure from the normal procedure of Acts 2:38?

   _____

2. Why does the book of Acts always link repentance with baptism?

   _____

God's covenant of grace is extended to the children of believers. Therefore, they have a right to that sign of covenant inclusion which, in the New Testament, is baptism.

1. Genesis 17:7—Who is included in God's covenant?

   _____

   Is this a temporary covenant?

   _____

   Are New Testament believers' children then under the covenant?

   _____

2. Acts 2:39—Of what does Peter assure believing parents here in this passage?

   _____

3. Genesis 17:11—What was the Old Testament sign of being included in the covenant of grace?

   _____

4. Colossians 2:11-12—What replaces the Old Testament circumcision as the New Testament sign of inclusion in the covenant of grace?

   _____

5. The New Testament teaches that the faith of a believing parent places his children in a unique relationship to God and His covenant.

   1 Corinthians 7:14—What is said of children who have at least one believing parent?

   _____

6. The New Testament makes reference to the baptism of households. The father's profession of faith is the only one noted by Scripture. It may be ordinarily assumed that these households included children.

a. Acts 16:15—Who was baptized on this occurrence?

_____

b. Acts 16:33—Who was baptized on this occurrence?

_____

For Discussion

1. In Reformed churches, what distinction is made between a baptized member and a communicant member?

2. Is there a practical difference for children of Christian parents if they are baptized in infancy or in later life? What is the significance of the statement in the *Larger Catechism* Question 165 that baptism is "a sign and seal of engrafting into Christ"?

3. How do you answer the charge that since the Bible does not specifically mention infant baptism, the Presbyterian view is adding to Scripture?

4. Why should the church baptize all children of believers when some obviously prove that they are not in the covenant in later life? (Relate this to the circumcision of Jacob and Esau.)

5. What does the *Larger Catechism* mean in Question 167 where it speaks of "improving" our baptism?

Digging Deeper...

1. John Murray, *Christian Baptism,* Presbyterian & Reformed, 95 pp. *A classic and convincing presentation of the Bible's teaching on the subject of baptism.*

2. Robert R. Booth, *Children of the Promise,* Presbyterian & Reformed, 190 pp. *By a former Baptist pastor.*

3. Rowland S. Ward, *Baptism in Scripture and History,* New Melbourne Press, 80 pp. *A fresh study of the meaning and mode of Christian baptism.*

The Sacraments (Part 2)

Memorize

Shorter Catechism

Q 96: What is the Lord's Supper?
A: The Lord's Supper is a Sacrament, wherein, by giving and receiving bread and wine, according to Christ's appointment, his death is showed forth; and the worthy receivers are, not after a corporal and carnal manner, but by faith, made partakers of his body and blood, with all his benefits, to their spiritual nourishment and growth in grace.

Q 97: What is required to the worthy receiving of the Lord's Supper?
A: It is required of them that would worthily partake of the Lord's Supper, that they examine themselves, of their knowledge to discern the Lord's body, of their faith to feed upon him, of the repentance, love, and new obedience; lest, coming unworthily, they eat and drink judgment to themselves.

Suggested Readings

Confession of Faith—Chapter 29
Reformed Presbyterian Testimony—Chapter 29

How Do You Understand the Lord's Supper?

Do You Think That:

_____ 1. The sacrament of communion is nothing more than symbol?

_____ 2. The church must offer communion to anyone who says he is a Christian?

_____ 3. People who have committed a serious, open sin should not commune even if they have confessed their action and repented of their sin?

_____ 4. Making communion a frequent occurrence decreases its spiritual significance?

The Lord's Supper

The Lord is spiritually present in the sacrament when the believer partakes in faith. The Lord's supper thus becomes a means of grace and spiritual strength to the believer.

Jesus established the Lord's supper as a perpetual memorial of His saving work.

1. Matthew 26:26-29—What does Jesus say of the bread of communion?

    _____

    What does He say of the wine in the cup?

    _____

2. 1 Corinthians 11:23-26—Why did Paul insist on the observance of the Lord's supper?

    _____

    What happens when we properly observe this sacrament? (v. 26)

    _____

    Note: Three basic views are held concerning the Lord's supper:

    a.. *A Memorial Only (Zwinglian View)*
        We profit only in the sense of rethinking the importance of Christ's death.

    b. *A Memorial and a Means of Grace through Faith (Reformed)*
        We feed on Christ spiritually and the benefits of His death are renewed in us by faith.

    c. *Automatic Grace (Roman Catholic & Lutheran View)*
        We actually receive Christ's physical body into our own and it works supernaturally to cleanse us.

The Lord's supper is to be received only by those who are able to discern its true meaning.

1. 1 Corinthians 11:28-29—What must a communicant do before communion?

    _____

    What must he avoid?

    _____

    What does it mean to "discern the Lord's body" (KJV)?

    _____

2. Luke 2:41-42—In what event does Jesus participate here for the first time?

    _____

How old was He?

_____

What is the significance of the Passover?

_____

How does it closely parallel the Lord's supper?

_____

Note: Jewish tradition admitted children to the Passover at age 12 when they were expected to discern its true meaning. The New Testament church has no set age requirement for communicant membership but requires that those who commune make a credible profession of saving faith.

The Lord's supper is to be carefully guarded by the Church as a whole.

1. God threatens personal judgment upon the unworthy partaker.

   1 Corinthians 11:29-30—What is the result of "not discerning the Lord's body"? (v. 29)

   _____

   How is this elaborated upon in verse 30?

   _____

   Note: This is commonly understood as referring to a physical illness and death.

2. The church must exercise authority in barring from her communion (membership) those who hold to false doctrine. By inference, then, she is also to bar from the Lord's supper (a special act of communion) those who hold to false doctrine.

   a. Titus 3:10—What does Paul require to be done here?

   _____

   b. 2 John 10-11—What is John's command concerning those who deny the doctrine of Christ?

   _____

3. The church must exclude from her membership and her table those who profess to be Christians but live immoral lives.

   a. 1 Corinthians 5:7-13—With what types of persons who call themselves brothers are Christians forbidden to eat?

   _____

b. 2 Thessalonians 3:6—How does Paul say we should act toward a brother who walks disorderly?

_____

Note: The church has traditionally administered the Lord's supper in one of three ways. See chart on page 61.

The means observed by some Reformed bodies, including the Reformed Presbyterian Church of North America, to guard the Lord's table is the practice of session-guarded communion.

1. Matthew 28:19-20—What does Jesus require of the church beyond evangelizing and baptizing her members?

_____

Is it biblical, then, for a church to require that her members profess a certain understanding of Christian doctrine before they are considered ready to commune?

_____

2. Acts 2:42—What was required of the early church in order to fellowship together in the "breaking of bread and prayers"?

_____

For Discussion

1. Why does Jesus allow Judas, whom He knows to be an unbeliever, to participate in the Lord's supper?

2. How does the existence of denominations affect the disciplinary aspect of the administration of the Lord's supper?

3. How explicit should a church be in setting forth her terms of communion?

4. Should the terms of receiving the Lord's supper be the same as the terms of membership?

Digging Deeper...

1. Gordon J. Keddie, *The Lord's Supper is a Celebration of Grace,* Evangelical Press, 96 pp. *Very useful examination of the spiritual meaning and efficacy of the sacrament.*

2. Thomas Doolittle, *A Treatise Concerning the Lord's Supper,* Soli Deo Gloria, 179 pp. *A wonderful older work that focuses on preparing the heart for coming to the Lord's table.*

3. RPC of Ireland ministers, *In Remembrance of Me: Book of Preparation for the Lord's Supper,* RPC of Ireland, 45 pp. *Designed for instructing covenant children in preparation for becoming communicant members.*

Traditional Ways Church Has Administered the Lord's Supper

	Open Communion	Close Communion	Session-Guarded Communion
Who May Commune?	Anyone who desires.	Members in good standing of certain denomination or congregation only.	Anyone who has publicly professed Christ.
What Standards Determine When an Individual Can Commune?	Individual conscience alone.	The individual conscience, the elders' judgment, and the denomination's theological standard.	Individual conscience with the elders' judgment.
What Methods Are Used to Determine a Person's Fitness?	Verbal warning and self-examination.	Verbal warning, self-examination, and oversight of the elders on the basis of denomination's theological standard.	Verbal warning, self-examination, plus an interview with the elders.
How Should We Assess This?	1. Denies scriptural duty of the Church (elders) to protect the table by action as well as words. 2. Weakens the authority of the Church as the "pillar and ground of the truth." 3. Stresses the importance of personal responsibility, but individualizes it to the exclusion of accountability before the whole church.	1. Denominational "agreement" tends to become standard, rather than agreement along with consistent practice. 2. Appears to be inconsistent to accept members who have not given unqualified allegiance to all the denominational doctrinal standards, while excluding from the table other believers outside the church because they cannot do so. 3. Provides a consistent biblical basis for fellowship among believers and for administration of discipline. 4. Effectively turns the Lord's table into the denomination's table, thereby denying the catholicity of the true Church of Jesus Christ.	1. Stresses the elders' role in properly administering the sacrament. 2. Maintains the proper balance between individual conscience before God and corporate accountability before the church. 3. Prevents the privatization of faith and roots its exercise in the body life of the visible church.

Eschatology

Memorize

Philippians 1:23
For I am hard-pressed between the two, having a desire to depart and be with Christ, which is far better.

Romans 8:11
But if the Spirit of Him who raised Jesus from the dead dwells in you, He who raised Christ from the dead will also give life to your mortal bodies through His spirit who dwells in you.

Shorter Catechism
Q. 37: What benefits do believers receive from Christ at death?
A: The souls of believers are, at their death, made perfect in holiness, and do immediately pass into glory; and their bodies, being still united to Christ, do rest in their graves until the resurrection.

Q. 38: What benefits do believers receive from Christ at the resurrection?
A: At the resurrection, believers, being raised up to glory, shall be openly acknowledged and acquitted in the day of judgment, and made perfectly blessed in the full enjoying of God to all eternity.

Suggested Readings
Confession of Faith—Chapters 32–33
Reformed Presbyterian Testimony—Chapters 32–33

What Happens When We Die (the Intermediate State)

The bodies of all men undergo corruption at death.

1. Genesis 3:19—What is God's announcement to Adam?

   _____

2. Acts 13:36-37—How are the deaths of David and Christ contrasted?

   _____

   Note: This is a fulfillment of Psalm 16:10.

The souls of all men maintain consciousness after death.

1. The souls of believers enter immediately into a state of blessedness.

    a. Job 19:26—What is Job's view of himself after death?

    _____

    b. Luke 23:43—What is Jesus' promise to the penitent thief?

    _____

    c. 2 Corinthians 5:8—What conviction concerning the intermediate state does Paul allude to here?

    _____

    d. Philippians 1:23—What does Paul consider to be "far better" here?

    _____

2. The souls of unbelievers are placed in torment at the time of death.

    a. Luke 16:19-31—What details in this passage show us that this has to be a reference to the conscious suffering of the unbeliever in hell before the final Judgment?

    _____

    b. 2 Peter 2:9—What is said about the unrighteous until the day of Judgment?

    _____

    Note: In properly interpreting a parable, it must be remembered that parables have one central theological thrust. Details and background are not to be given forced theological interpretations. In Luke 16 references to the physical bodies of Dives (the rich man) and Lazarus should not be forced to infer the uniting of the body and soul before the final resurrection. Berkhof says, "The Bible sheds very little direct light on the state of the wicked between death and the resurrection. . . .The only passage that can really come into consideration here is the parable of the rich man and Lazarus in Luke 16, where 'hades' denotes hell, the place of eternal torment. The rich man found himself in the place of torment; his condition was fixed forever; and he was conscious of his miserable plight, sought mitigation of the pain he was suffering, and desired to have his brethren warned, in order that they might avoid a similar doom. In addition to this direct proof there is also an inferential proof. If the righteous enter upon their eternal state at once, the presumption is that this is true of the wicked as well" (*Systematic Theology,* p. 680).

The Second Coming of Christ

The visible, historical return of Christ is prophesied in Scripture.

1. Acts 1:11—What were the disciples promised by the two angels?

    _____

2. Titus 2:13—What does Paul say believers look for?

    _____

3. 1 Thessalonians 4:16—What details do we learn here about Christ's return?

    _____

Several types of events must be fulfilled before Christ's return.

1. The calling of the Gentiles

    a. Isaiah 60:1-3—What is the future of the Gentiles in the Kingdom?

        _____

    b. Romans 11:25—What does Paul prophesy for the Gentile nations?

        _____

2. The mass conversion of Israel

    a. Romans 11:1-2—What is Paul stating here?

        _____

    b. Romans 11:25-29—What is Paul's line of argument here?

        _____

    Note: Some scholars interpret this passage to refer to "spiritual Israel" or the New Testament church, but the editors of this manual do not share this contention. Paul is not prophesying the conversion of every single Jew when he speaks of "all Israel" being saved any more than he refers to the conversion of every last Gentile. He does, however, refer to a widespread return of the Jewish people to true covenant relationship through Christ. This chapter does _not,_ on the other hand, teach the reestablishment of an earthly Jewish monarchy and revived temple worship under Christ in some future millennial kingdom.

3. Apostasy and tribulation climaxing before Christ's return

a. Revelation 20:7-8—What is foretold here?

_____

When is this to take place?

_____

b. Revelation 20:9-10—Will this final uprising be successful?

_____

4. The appearing of "the man of sin"

a. 2 Thessalonians 2:1-4—What does Paul say must happen before Christ returns?

_____

How does he describe the "man of sin"?

_____

b. 2 Thessalonians 2:8-9—What does Paul say will occur?

_____

5. The defeat of the enemies of Jesus Christ

a. Psalm 110:1-2—What is described here?

_____

b. 1 Corinthians 15:24-26—What does Paul say must happen before the end comes?

_____

The Millennium

Note: Evangelical Christians are not in full agreement concerning the time of Christ's return and the "millennial age" referred to in Revelation 20. The four views commonly expressed are known as Premillennialism, Dispensationalism, Postmillennialism, and Amillennialism. In the section below, you will find brief descriptions of each of these views and a brief evaluation. Readers are encouraged to read through this section carefully in order to become adequately acquainted with each view. We are indebted to G.I. Williamson for the diagrams used here from his work on the *Confession of Faith.*

The Postmillennial View of the Second Coming

1. Statement of the view:

a. Considers the millennial age to be the present period rather than a literal 1,000-year future event.

b. Satan is now bound and unable to thwart the plan and purpose of Christ, the resurrected King of glory who now reigns. (See John 12:31; Heb. 2:14)

c. Widespread triumph of Christianity before Christ returns and a Golden Age is issued in.

d. Golden Age viewed by some as following the great apostasy of the fall of Jerusalem.

e. Other Postmillennialists look for a future period of apostasy following the Golden Age.

f. Jews will be converted as a nation.

g. Church (kingdom) will be established in great power when Christ returns.

h. There will be only one return of Christ. At this time, the general judgment of all men will take place.

i. At the return of Christ, there will be one final resurrection of both saved and lost.

2. Diagram of this view:

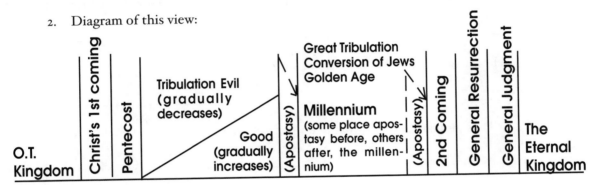

3. Strengths of this view:

a. Takes seriously the optimistic prophecies of the world-changing power of the gospel.

b. Sees Christ, not Satan, as the Victor in history as well as eternity.

c. Provides a compelling hope and motivation to labor vigorously for the advancement of the all-encompassing Kingdom of Christ.

The Amillennial View of the Second Coming

1. Statement of the view:

a. Considers the millennial age to be the present period rather than a literal 1,000-year future event.

b. Satan is now bound and unable to thwart the plan and purpose of Christ, the resurrected King of glory who now reigns. (See John 12:81; Heb. 2:14)

c. Denies the Golden Age optimism of the postmillennialist.

d. Some amillennialists see a continuing of tribulation and apostasy until Christ returns with no particular heightened persecution or definite signs of His coming.

e. Other amillennialists look for definite signs of Christ's return, such as a heightened tribulation, a specific Man of Sin, and a general conversion of the Jews.

f. There will be only one return of Christ. At this time, the general judgment of all men will take place.

g. At the return of Christ, there will be one final resurrection of both saved and lost.

2. Strengths of this view:

    a. Maintains the biblical anticipation of a general resurrection of the just and the unjust.
    b. Takes seriously the continued existence of wheat and tares, righteous and wicked, until the harvest at the end of the age.
    c. Seems to account for the expectation of continued persecution of the saints in all ages.

The Premillennial View of the Second Coming

1. Statement of the view:

    Christ will return following the Tribulation to:

    a. resurrect the saints;
    b. bind Satan to give opportunity for more conversions;
    c. reign for 1,000 years on earth with Jerusalem as His capital;
    d. judge the wicked at the end of that millennium and establish the new heavens and the new earth of 1 Peter 3.

2. Diagram of this view:

O.T. Kingdom	Christ's 1st coming	Pentecost	Age of Good and Evil	Apostasy-Antichrist	2nd Coming of Christ	Saints' resurrection	Millennium (Christ's 1,000-year reign on earth)	Resurrection of lost	Judgment of wicked	The Eternal Kingdom

3. Weaknesses of this view:

    a. Based on forced literalistic interpretation of certain Old Testament prophecies, but not *all* of them.
    b   Insists Revelation 20:1-6 is literal, even though it describes a scene in heaven and makes no mention of the Jews or Palestine.
    c. Makes the Kingdom of God a future earthly kingdom while the New Testament represents it as spiritual, heavenly and already in existence. (See Matt. 11:12; 12:28; 2 Tim. 4:18)
    d. Denies the general resurrection (Matt. 25:31-46) and teaches two separate resurrections.

The Dispensational Premillennial View of the Second Coming

1. Statement of the view:

    A specialized form of premillennialism that emphasizes the role of Israel in prophecy. Its outstanding points include chronologically:

a. The viewing of the gospel or Church Age as a parenthesis between Christ's comings.
b. The immediate return of Christ *for* His saints (called the any-moment Rapture) before the Tribulation.
c. A seven-year period of tribulation when Anti-Christ is revealed.
d. Another return of Christ *with* His saints to destroy Anti-Christ and bind Satan.
e. A revived Jewish empire and temple worship under Christ for 1,000 years.
f. The loosing of Satan for a short time after the Millennium and the final battle of Armageddon.
g. The destruction of the world and the beginning of the eternal kingdom.

2. Diagram of this view:

3. Weaknesses of this view:

a. Has same weaknesses as those stated above concerning premillennialism.
b. Destroys the biblical concept of the Church as the agent of Christ's Kingdom by making the Kingdom totally future.
c. By its insistence on the any-moment Rapture, Dispensationalism thrives on sensationalism, distorts historical details, and creates unwarranted fear/hope.

The Final State (the condition of man after the Second Coming)

There will be one final judgment of both saved and lost, dead and living.

1. 1 Thessalonians 4:15-17—What happens to the dead at Christ's return?

_____

What happens to the living?

_____

2. 2 Corinthians 5: 10—What does Paul say will happen to all at Christ's return?

_____

3. Matthew 25:31-46—How is the judgment pictured here?

_____

The bodies of all the dead (saved and lost) will be raised up at Christ's return.

1. Daniel 12:2—What is said of the dead here?

    _____

2. John 5:28-29—What types of resurrection will there be?

    _____

    Is this presented as two separate events?

    _____

3. Acts 24:15—Who will participate in the final resurrection?

    _____

The righteous dead will receive resurrection bodies and live with Christ eternally in His Kingdom. Thus, heaven is a place, not merely a condition.

1. 1 Corinthians 15:22-23, 35, 42, 44—What do these verses tell us about the body at the resurrection?

    _____

    _____

2. Philippians 3:21—What will Christ do to the bodies of believers?

    _____

The unrighteous who are "resurrected unto judgment" (John 5:29) will be eternally separated from Christ and eternally punished. Hell is also a place and not merely a state or condition.

1. Matthew 13:42—How is hell described here?

    _____

2. Matthew 8:12-13—What does Jesus say here about future punishment?

    _____

3. Matthew 25:46—What adjective is used to describe the punishment of the wicked?

    _____

Both the righteous and the lost will receive degrees of reward and punishment respectively.

1. Luke 19:11-26—What is taught concerning this parable about the faithful stewards?

_____

2. Luke 12:47-48—What is said about the punishment of the willfully disobedient?

_____

For Discussion

1. Does Scripture teach purgatory or a "second chance"?

2. To what event(s) does Jesus refer in Matthew 24? What implications, if any, does this passage have for eschatology?

3. How do you explain passages like Matthew 16:28; 1 John 2:18, which speak of Christ's coming as near?

4. What basic propositions must all biblical Christians believe concerning Christ's return?

Digging Deeper...

1. Cornelius P. Venema, *The Promise of the Future,* Banner of Truth, 538 pp. *A comprehensive survey of the Bible's teaching on the Last Things.*

2. Edward Donnelly, *Heaven and Hell,* Banner of Truth, 127 pp. *Excellent treatment of the final state by Reformed Presbyterian pastor in Belfast, N. Ireland.*

3. Iain Murray, *The Puritan Hope,* Banner of Truth, 265 pp. *Employs both exposition of Scripture and historical material to make the case that it is not "orthodox" to hold a gloomy prospect for the future of Christianity.*

The Westminster Confession of Faith
(Adopted 1648)

and

The Testimony of the Reformed Presbyterian Church of North America
(Adopted August 1980)

In Parallel Columns

CONFESSION

TESTIMONY

Introduction

1. God's covenants are His gracious instruments for the accomplishment of His purpose that the creation should serve Him. The covenant character of revelation appears in all the Scripture and binds the sixty-six books together in one unified Word of God. It gives the two divisions of the Bible their names, the Old Testament and the New Testament, or Covenant (Jer. 31:31-33; Heb. 8:13). The covenant concept lies at the heart of the *Westminster Confession of Faith* and the *Testimony of the Reformed Presbyterian Church of North America.*

2. Covenant revelation began with God's first conversation with man. God made him ruler over all things, His servant and colaborer in achieving His purpose for the creation (Gen. 2:15). This covenant directed man's activity and promised him life through obedience to God's Word. Thus it was a "Covenant of Life" (*Shorter Catechism* 12), confirmed by the curse of death for disobedience. By work and rest, after the pattern of his Creator, man was to demonstrate his dependence on God and his hope of final consummation of God's purpose. This covenant required man to respond to God to the full capacity of his being as the image of God.

3. When Adam broke the covenant by disobedience death came upon him and all mankind since they were included in the covenant. But God delayed the final sentence of death, and promised victory over Satan through the seed of the woman. Man's mandate to subdue the earth continued, but he must toil in grief under the curse that God placed upon the whole creation. God's purpose for creation would be accomplished through the Covenant of Grace.

4. The remainder of Scripture is the gradual unfolding of the Covenant of Grace through a series of covenants, each developing a particular element of the one preceding it and preparing for a more complete accomplishment. The call of the elect people, ultimately to include all nations, to live by faith in obedience was set forth in successive covenants made with Abraham, the nation of Israel, and David.

5. In the fulness of time God brought forth His Son, born of a virgin, of the seed of David. He obeyed the Covenant of Life on behalf of His people and offered Himself as a sacrifice to die, once for all, in their place and to appear for them on the throne of God in heaven. Thus Jesus obeyed as man, died for man and sat down in heaven to rule over all things and bring His covenant people to share His throne and glory (Luke 22:30).

6. In the Covenant of Grace all men are called to repentance and obedience. By the grace of God through the merit of Christ and the convicting work of the Holy Spirit, God's people are saved, sanctified (Lev. 22:32; Heb. 2:11), and given one mind and heart to serve Him. Thus God is always reaching out to men. The covenant people are bound to one another in their Head, Jesus Christ. They are children of the covenant bearing witness corporately to His lordship over every sphere of their life. There is nothing outside of His dominion.

7. Israel frequently responded to God by covenanting with Him to live in faithfulness to the covenant given through Moses (Josh. 24), or to bring about reform after apostasy (2 Chron. 15:12; 29:10; 34:29-32; Neh. 9:38). These were solemn agreements between the people and God that they would observe His revealed law in particular circumstances in their day (Neh. 9:38; 10:29). Though these are covenants, they are to be distinguished from the covenants given by God to Adam, Noah, Abraham, Israel, David and from the new covenant.

8. The whole creation is under God's covenant to accomplish His will through Christ, the Mediator, by the Holy Spirit (Gen. 9:9-16; Ps. 114; Jer. 33:20-21; Rom. 8:20-22).

Explanation

9. *The Westminster Confession of Faith* is one of the historic creeds of the Presbyterian and Reformed churches. The Reformed Presbyterian Church of North America believes that this *Confession* is based on, and subordinate to, Scripture. The truth it presents is of inestimable value for contemporary society.

10. However, changes in the application of truth are needed because of changing situations in each generation. Some

current topics of vital importance for the Christian Church were unknown in the 17th century. Therefore, the Reformed Presbyterian Church of North America presents its *Testimony* applying Scripture truth to the contemporary situation. This *Testimony* is placed in a column parallel to that which contains the *Confession*.

11. Wherever applicable, to aid in the usefulness of these documents, notations are made at the heading of each chapter to the *Larger* and *Shorter Catechisms*. As a general rule, proof texts are provided for the positive statements, but not for the rejections.

12. All of these documents, the *Westminster Confession of Faith,* the *Testimony of the Reformed Presbyterian Church,* and the *Larger* and *Shorter Catechisms,* are of equal authority in the church; except that where noted, earlier documents are to be interpreted by the later ones.

Chapter 1: Of the Holy Scripture

(Larger Catechism: 2-5; Shorter Catechism: 2-3)

1. God has revealed Himself in His works, called natural or general revelation, and His Word, called special revelation. This self-revelation contains all that man needs to know about God. The revelation of God in His works is clear, but it does not make known the covenant purposes of God. Hence, God began, from the creation of man, to make known the covenant relationship He had established between Himself and man. These matters could not have become known to man except by special (verbal) revelation.
1 Cor. 2:9; Gen. 1:28; Gen. 2:16-17; Rom. 1:19-20.

2. These two forms of revelation, His works and His Word, are complementary. Any apparent obscurity of either of them, or alleged confusion or contradiction between them, arises from the natural limitations of man, and especially from his sinful state of rebellion against God, and the resultant curse of God upon him and the whole creation. The Scripture reveals that both the works of God and the written Word of God have been spoken into being by the Son, the living Word of God, the Creator, who also, as the incarnate Mediator and risen Savior continues to uphold the universe by His powerful Word.
Ps. 19; Job 38-41; Ps. 139:6; Rom. 1:19-32; John 1:1-3; Heb. 1:1-3.

1. Although the light of nature and the works of creation and providence do so far manifest the goodness, wisdom, and power of God, as to leave men unexcusable; yet are they not sufficient to give that knowledge of God and of His will, which is necessary unto salvation. Therefore it pleased the Lord, at sundry times, and in divers manners, to reveal Himself, and to declare that His will unto His Church; and afterwards, for the better preserving and propagating of the truth, and for the more sure establishment and comfort of the Church against the corruption of the flesh, and the malice of Satan and of the world, to commit the same wholly unto writing: which maketh the Holy Scripture to be most necessary; those former ways of God's revealing His will unto His people being now ceased.
Rom. 2:14-15; Rom. 1:19-20; Ps. 19:1-3; Rom. 1:32 with 2:1; 1 Cor. 1:21; 1 Cor. 2:13-14; Heb. 1:1; Prov. 22:19-21; Luke 1:3-4; Rom. 15:4; Matt. 4:4, 7, 10; Isa. 8:19-20; 2 Tim. 3:15; 2 Pet. 1:19; Heb. 1:1-2.

3. The revelation of God's works can be rightly understood only in the light of the written Word.
1 Cor. 1:21.

4. The living Word became man, Jesus Christ. In His life, death and resurrection He fulfilled the covenant broken by man's disobedience and did most completely reveal God and His purpose for man. The Son makes the Father known to man; yet the Son is not known by man except by the Spirit through the Scripture. Hence, the Scripture is the final word of God to man for faith and life.
Matt. 11:27; John 1:18; John 14:24-26; 1 Cor. 2:10-13.

5. God gave His written revelation progressively by holy men whom He chose, and inspired and infallibly guided to write inerrantly and completely the revelation of His will. No further such revelation is to be received. The human authors with differing skills expressed themselves in the peculiar idioms and a variety of literary forms common to their times. They used human sources of historical information and they recorded interpretations of those events and prophecies concerning the future that God revealed to them. In all they wrote, however, they were guided by the Holy Spirit as to matter and manner

so that their writings are indeed the Word of God.
Gen. 2:4; Gen. 5:1; Gen. 6:9; 1 Kings 11:41; 1 Kings 14:29; 2 Sam. 23:1-2; 2 Tim. 3:16; 2 Pet. 1:21; Jer. 36:32.

6. *We reject* any view of Scripture that denies the objective truth of the Bible by making the authority of its message dependent on the circumstances or the subjective experience of the reader.

7. *We reject* the notion that the process of revelation was a mechanical one in which the writers were reduced to mere stenographers.

8. *We also reject* all theories of composition that make the writers mere editors or collectors of human tradition and liturgy, so that their writings are but human accounts or interpretations of religious development under God.

9. *We reject* the teaching that prophecy is history written after the event.

2. Under the name of Holy Scripture, or the Word of God written, are now contained all the books of the Old and New Testaments, which are these:

Of the Old Testament:

Genesis	Ecclesiastes
Exodus	The Song of Songs
Leviticus	Isaiah
Numbers	Jeremiah
Deuteronomy	Lamentations
Joshua	Ezekiel
Judges	Daniel
Ruth	Hosea
1 Samuel	Joel
2 Samuel	Amos
1 Kings	Obadiah
2 Kings	Jonah
1 Chronicles	Micah
2 Chronicles	Nahum
Ezra	Habakkuk
Nehemiah	Zephaniah
Esther	Haggai
Job	Zechariah
Psalms	Malachi
Proverbs	

Of the New Testament:

Matthew	1 Timothy
Mark	2 Timothy
Luke	Titus
John	Philemon
Acts	Hebrews

Romans	James
1 Corinthians	1 Peter
2 Corinthians	2 Peter
Galatians	1 John
Ephesians	2 John
Philippians	3 John
Colossians	Jude
1 Thessalonians	Revelation
2 Thessalonians	

All which are given by inspiration of God, to be the rule of faith and life.
Luke 16:29, 31; Eph. 2:20; Rev. 22:18-19; 2 Tim. 3:16.

3. The books commonly called Apocrypha, not being of divine inspiration, are no part of the canon of the Scripture; and therefore are of no authority in the Church of God, nor to be any otherwise approved, or made use of, than other human writings.
Luke 24:27, 44; Rom. 3:2; 2 Pet. 1:21.

4. The authority of the Holy Scripture, for which it ought to be believed and obeyed, dependeth not upon the testimony of any man, or church; but wholly upon God (who is truth itself) the author thereof: and therefore it is to be received because it is the Word of God.
2 Pet. 1:19, 21; 2 Tim. 3:16; 1 John 5:9; 1 Thess. 2:13.

5. We may be moved and induced by the testimony of the Church to a high and reverent esteem of the Holy Scripture. And the heavenliness of the matter, the efficacy of the doctrine, the majesty of the style, the consent of all the parts, the scope of the whole (which is, to give all glory to God), the full discovery it makes of the only way of man's salvation, the many other incomparable excellencies, and the entire perfection thereof, are arguments whereby it doth abundantly evidence itself to be the Word of God: yet notwithstanding, our full persuasion and assurance of the infallible truth and divine authority thereof, is from the inward work of the Holy Spirit bearing witness by and with the Word in our hearts.
1 Tim. 3:15; 1 John 2:20, 27; John 16:13-14; 1 Cor. 2:10-12; Isa. 59:21.

6. The whole counsel of God concerning all things necessary for His own glory, man's salvation, faith, and life, is either expressly set down in Scripture, or by good and necessary consequence may be deduced from Scripture: unto which nothing at any time is to be added, whether by new revelations of the Spirit, or traditions of men. Nevertheless we acknowledge the inward illumination of the Spirit of God to be necessary for the saving understanding of such things as are revealed in the Word: and that there are some circum-

10. The Old Testament is the word of Christ and is of equal authority with the New Testament. Nor are the earthly words of Christ quoted in the Scriptures in any way of greater authority or of greater significance to the Church than the rest of God's Word. It is the triune God who speaks with equal and absolute authority in and through every part of Scripture.

11. The truthfulness of God, and not the reasonableness of any doctrine, is the ground of our faith. It is the work of the Gospel to cast down reasonings against the knowledge of God, and to take every thought captive to the obedience of Christ.
1 Cor. 2:15; 2 Cor. 10:5.

12. *We reject* the view that the Bible sets forth truth in the form of myth.

13. *We reject* the view that the Bible is only partially inspired, that inspiration pertains only to "revelational" matters, or "saving" truth, or that the Bible as originally given contains any inaccuracy in fact or history.

14. *We reject* the view that the Holy Spirit gives personal revelations or that He leads men apart from the general principles of the Word or contrary to its teachings.

stances concerning the worship of God, and government of the Church, common to human actions and societies, which are to be ordered by the light of nature and Christian prudence, according to the general rules of the Word, which are always to be observed.
2 Tim. 3:15-17; Gal. 1:8-9; 2 Thess. 2:2; John 6:45; 1 Cor. 2:9-12; 1 Cor. 11:13-14; 1 Cor. 14:26, 40.

15. *We reject* the concept that there is continuing revelation of God in the actions, decisions or decrees of the Church.

7. All things in Scripture are not alike plain in themselves, nor alike clear unto all: yet those things which are necessary to be known, believed, and observed for salvation, are so clearly propounded and opened in some place of Scripture or other, that not only the learned, but the unlearned, in a due use of the ordinary means, may attain unto a sufficient understanding of them.
2 Pet. 3:16; Ps. 119:105, 130.

16. There are in the Scripture doctrines which unassisted reason could never have discovered; and yet, when revealed, are perfectly intelligible by the human mind. Other doctrines are taught in Scripture which human reason cannot fully comprehend and which must be received on the authority of God.
Isa. 40:13; 1 Cor. 1:20; Ps. 119:130; 1 Cor. 2:6-16.

17. *We reject* any suggestion that God uses human reason on a level with Scripture to reveal His truth.

8. The Old Testament in Hebrew (which was the native language of the people of God of old), and the New Testament in Greek (which at the time of the writing of it was most generally known to the nations), being immediately inspired by God, and by His singular care and providence kept pure in all ages, are therefore authentical; so as, in all controversies of religion, the Church is finally to appeal unto them. But, because these original tongues are not known to all the people of God, who have a right unto, and interest in the Scriptures, and are commanded, in the fear of God, to read and search them, therefore they are to be translated into the vulgar language of every nation unto which they come, that the Word of God dwelling plentifully in all, they may worship Him in an acceptable manner; and, through patience and comfort of the Scriptures, may have hope.
Matt. 5:18; Isa. 8:20; Acts 15:15; John 5:39, 46; 1 Cor. 14:6, 9, 11-12, 24, 27-28; Col. 3:16; Rom. 15:4.

18. Bible translations must combine faithfulness to the original text with the idiom of the native language, and thus will always be imperfect. The Church is responsible to examine the documents available to determine as far as possible what was originally written, and to study the translations as to their accuracy in conveying the meaning of the original, and to advise the public concerning them. Paraphrases, which interpret rather than translate, must be used with great caution.

9. The infallible rule of interpretation of Scripture is the Scripture itself: and therefore, when there is a question about the true and full sense of any Scripture (which is not manifold, but one) it must be searched and known by other places that speak more clearly.
2 Pet. 1:20-21; Acts 15:15-16.

10. The supreme judge by which all controversies of religion are to be determined, and all decrees of councils, opinions of ancient writers, doctrines of men, and private spirits, are to be examined; and in whose sentence we are to rest; can be no other but the Holy Spirit speaking in the Scripture.
Matt. 22:29, 31; Eph. 2:20 with Acts 28:25.

19. All men have the right to read the Bible, to inquire into its meaning, and to adopt the doctrines it teaches. In studying the Bible men must depend upon the illumination of the Holy Spirit. They must use God-given human faculties and search in earnest for the truth, in submission to the authority of Scripture. In interpreting the Bible consideration must be given to the historical situation in which the passage was written, to the grammatical structure, and to the literary form. The instruction and counsel of fellow believers, of teachers of the Word, and creeds and confessions of the Church should be given due consideration. When men understand the message of the Bible, they must earnestly seek to obey that message in all that they think and do.
Acts 2:42; John 5:39; 2 Tim. 2:15; Acts 17:11.

Chapter 2: Of God, and of the Holy Trinity

(Larger Catechism: 7-11; Shorter Catechism: 4-6)

1. There is but one only, living, and true God: who is infinite in being and perfection, a most pure spirit, invisible, without body, parts, or passions, immutable, immense, eternal, incomprehensible, almighty, most wise, most holy, most free, most absolute, working all things according to the counsel of His own immutable and most righteous will, for His own glory; most loving, gracious, merciful, long-suffering, abundant in goodness and truth, forgiving iniquity, transgression, and sin; the rewarder of them that diligently seek Him; and withal, most just and terrible in His judgments, hating all sin, and who will by no means clear the guilty.
Deut. 6:4, 1 Cor. 8:4, 6; 1 Thess. 1:9; Jer. 10:10; Job 11:7-9; Job 26:14; John 4:24; 1 Tim. 1:17; Deut. 4:15-16; John 4:24 with Luke 24:39; Acts 14:11, 15; Jas. 1:17; Mal. 3:6; 1 Kings 8:27; Jer. 23:23-24; Ps. 90:2; 1 Tim. 1:17; Ps. 145:3; Gen. 17:1; Rev. 4:8; Rom. 16:27; Isa. 6:3; Rev. 4:8; Ps. 115:3; Ex. 3:14; Eph. 1:11; Prov. 16:4; Rom. 11:36; 1 John 4:8, 16; Ex. 34:6-7; Heb. 11:6; Neh. 9:32-33; Ps. 5:5-6; Nah. 1:2-3; Ex. 34:7.

1. The true God is revealed in Scripture. Any concept of God, however sincerely held, that is contrary to Scripture is false, and in the end idolatrous. A knowledge of the true God is essential to saving faith.
Rom. 10:14-17; Isa. 44:6, 10-17; Acts 17:22-29.

2. God hath all life, glory, goodness, blessedness, in and of Himself; and is alone in and unto Himself all-sufficient, not standing in need of any creatures which He hath made, nor deriving any glory from them, but only manifesting His own glory in, by, unto, and upon them: He is the alone fountain of all being, of whom, through whom, and to whom are all things; and hath most sovereign dominion over them, to do by them, for them, or upon them whatsoever Himself pleaseth. In His sight all things are open and manifest; His knowledge is infinite, infallible, and independent upon the creature, so as nothing is to Him contingent, or uncertain. He is most holy in all His counsels, in all His works, and in all His commands. To Him is due from angels and men, and every other creature, whatsoever worship, service or obedience He is pleased to require of them.
John 5:26; Acts 7:2; Ps. 119:68; 1 Tim. 6:15; Rom. 9:5; Acts 17:24-25; Job 22:2-3; Rom. 11:36; Rev. 4:11; 1 Tim. 6:15; Dan. 4:25, 35; Heb. 4:13; Rom. 11:33-34; Ps. 147:5; Acts 15:18; Ezek. 11:5; Ps. 145:17; Rom. 7:12; Rev. 5:12-14.

2. *We reject* any teaching which denies or obscures the difference between God the Creator and man the creature or the rest of creation.
Rom. 1:23-25; Acts 5:3-4.

3. In the unity of the Godhead there be three persons, of one substance, power, and eternity; God the Father, God the Son, and God the Holy Ghost. The Father is of none, neither begotten, nor proceeding: the Son is eternally begotten of the Father: the Holy Ghost eternally proceeding from the Father and the Son.
1 John 5:7; Matt. 3:16-17; Matt. 28:19; 2 Cor. 13:14; John 1:14, 18; John 15:26; Gal. 4:6.

3. God the Father, God the Son and God the Holy Spirit are equally to be worshipped by angels and men.
Phil. 2:9-10; Heb. 1:2-3, 6, 8; 2 Cor. 13:14.

4. The doctrine of the Trinity is knowable only by special revelation. It is not possible for an explanation or comparison from any other source to serve as a true representation of this doctrine.
Isa. 40:18; Isa. 46:5; 1 Cor. 2:10-13; John 1:18.

5. *We reject* any teaching which subordinates any person of the Godhead as to substance, power or glory.
John 1:1-2; Acts 5:3-4.

6. The Holy Spirit, the third Person of the Trinity, proceeds from the Father and the Son, and is truly God, of the same substance, equal in power and glory with the Father and the Son. He is to be believed in, loved, obeyed and worshipped by men in all ages.
2 Cor. 13:14; John 14:26; Matt. 28:19; Luke 1:35; Heb. 10:29; Rev. 22:17; Eph. 2:18-22; John 16:7; Gal. 4:6; Acts 5:3-4; Acts 16:6-7; Mark 3:29; Rom. 8:26-27; 1 John 2:20-27.

7. The Holy Spirit, as the giver of life, is everywhere present and makes manifest the grace of God toward all His creatures. He supplies man's powers of reason and conscience, restrains His disposition toward evil, and preserves a degree of justice and morality in society. His common work for all mankind does not regenerate but leaves those who reject God without excuse.
Gen. 1:2; Job 33:4; Ps. 104:30; Job 34:14-15; Gen. 6:3; Isa. 32:15-17; Rom. 1:20.

8. The special work of the Holy Spirit is to apply to the elect the redeeming benefits of Christ's atonement. The outward and ordinary means through which He communicates the knowledge of redemption is the written Word, in which is infallibly recorded the will of God for man's salvation. He prepares for the reception of the Word and accompanies it with His persuasive power. He regenerates the elect by His grace, convicts them of sin, moves them to repentance and persuades and enables them to embrace Christ through faith. In regeneration He works secretly, supernaturally and effectually. This work is in itself so distinct and necessary, that without it, no evidence of the truth of the Gospel, no power of argument, no persuasion of love or of terror, no human eloquence, no combination of the most favorable circumstances, can be effectual in producing salvation.
John 3:1-8; Acts 2:38; 1 Cor. 12:3; 2 Pet. 1:21; 2 Sam. 23:2; John 7:39; John 16:13; Titus 3:5; Ezek. 36:27; 1 John 4:2; Gal. 4:6; 2 Thess. 2:13.

9. The Holy Spirit in uniting all believers to Christ, dwells in them as their Comforter, guiding, teaching and performing in them all those gracious activities by which they are sanctified and sealed unto the day of redemption. His guidance and teaching cannot contradict anything written in God's Word, but makes known the will of God to His people through prayer and submission to the Word.
Rom. 8:14, 26-27; 1 Cor. 2:12-16; Eph. 4:30; 2 Tim. 3:16-17; Rom. 15:4; John 16:5-11.

10. *We reject* the teaching that inner light, dreams, visions

or charismatic gifts provide a new, more advanced or infallible revelation of God.

11. The sin against the Holy Spirit which will not be forgiven, commonly called the unpardonable sin, is the final—secret or open—rejection of His testimony concerning Jesus Christ. It is a sin unto death, because it is blasphemy against the Holy Spirit, and because, by its very nature, it is the willful and persistent rejection of the only hope of forgiveness through the Savior. On the other hand, the fear of having committed this sin, together with an earnest desire for fellowship with God in Christ, give evidence that this sin has not been committed.
1 Thess. 5:19; Acts 7:51; Heb. 10:26-29; Matt. 12:31-32; Mark 3:28-30; Luke 12:8-10; 1 Cor. 12:3; 1 John 5:16; Heb. 6:4-6; 1 John 2:22; 1 John 4:3; Isa. 50:10; 1 John 1:7; Heb. 6:9-11.

12. The Holy Spirit, abiding in believers, unites them to Christ the Head, and to one another in the Church which is His body. He imparts various gifts and graces to all her members that they may serve Christ. He calls and fits His servants for their work, and qualifies all officers of the Church for their particular tasks. He makes effective the Word and the ordinances of the Gospel. By Christ working through His Spirit, the Church will be preserved, increased, purified, and, at last, made perfectly holy in the presence of God to all eternity.
Eph. 2:14-18; Eph. 4:1-5; Acts 2:4; 1 Cor. 12; Acts 13:2; 2 Pet. 1:19-21; 1 Thess. 1:5-6; John 20:22-23; Matt. 16:18; Matt. 28:19-20.

13. *We reject* the view that the work of the Holy Spirit is limited to individuals.
Rev. 2:11.

14. *We reject* the teaching that some true believers have not received the Holy Spirit.

15. *We reject* the teaching that particular charismatic gifts such as those of tongues and of healing are normal or necessary signs of being filled with the Holy Spirit.

Chapter 3: Of God's Eternal Decree

(Larger Catechism: 12-14; Shorter Catechism: 7-8)

1. God from all eternity did, by the most wise and holy counsel of His own will, freely, and unchangeably ordain whatsoever comes to pass: yet so, as thereby neither is God the author of sin, nor is violence offered to the will of the creatures, nor is the liberty or contingency of second causes taken away, but rather established.
Eph. 1:11; Rom. 11:33; Heb. 6:17; Rom. 9:15, 18; Jas. 1:13, 17; 1 John 1:5; Acts 2:23; Matt. 17:12; Acts 4:27-28; John 19:11; Prov. 16:33.

1. *We reject* any teaching which asserts that God has not planned all that comes to pass.

2. Although God knows whatsoever may or can come to pass upon all supposed conditions, yet hath He not decreed anything because He foresaw it as future, or as that which would come to pass upon such conditions.
Acts 15:18; 1 Sam. 23:11-12; Matt. 11:21, 23; Rom. 9:11, 13, 16, 18.

2. It is God's decree which by itself completely determines the course of history; it is never the course of history which in any way determines or modifies God's decree.

3. By the decree of God, for the manifestation of His glory, some men and angels are predestinated unto everlasting life, and others fore-ordained to everlasting death.
1 Tim. 5:21; Matt. 25:41; Rom. 9:22-23; Eph. 1:5-6; Prov. 16:4.

4. These angels and men, thus predestinated and fore-ordained, are particularly and unchangeably designed, and their number is so certain and definite, that it cannot be either increased or diminished.
2 Tim. 2:19; John 13:18.

5. Those of mankind that are predestinated unto life, God, before the foundation of the world was laid, according to His eternal and immutable purpose, and the secret counsel and good pleasure of His will, hath chosen, in Christ, unto everlasting glory, out of His mere free grace and love, without any foresight of faith or good works, or perseverance in either of them, or any other thing in the creature, as conditions, or causes moving Him thereunto: and all to the praise of His glorious grace.
Eph. 1:4, 9, 11; Rom. 8:30; 2 Tim. 1:9; 1 Thess. 5:9; Rom. 9:11, 13, 16; Eph. 1:4, 9; Eph. 1:6, 12.

6. As God hath appointed the elect unto glory, so hath He, by the eternal and most free purpose of His will, foreordained all the means thereunto. Wherefore they who are elected, being fallen in Adam, are redeemed by Christ, are effectually called unto faith in Christ by His Spirit working in due season, are justified, adopted, sanctified, and kept by His power through faith unto salvation. Neither are any other redeemed by Christ, effectually called, justified, adopted,

sanctified, and saved, but the elect only.
1 Pet. 1:2; Eph. 1:4-5; Eph. 2:10; 2 Thess. 2:13; 1 Thess. 5:9-10; Titus 2:14; Rom. 8:30; Eph. 1:5; 2 Thess. 2:13; 1 Pet. 1:5; John 17:9; Rom. 8:28-39; John 6:64-65; John 10:26; John 8:47; 1 John 2:19.

7. The rest of mankind God was pleased, according to the unsearchable counsel of His own will, whereby He extendeth or withholdeth mercy, as He pleaseth, for the glory of His sovereign power over His creatures, to pass by; and to ordain them to dishonour and wrath, for their sin, to the praise of His glorious justice.
Matt. 11:25-26; Rom. 9:17-18, 21-22; 2 Tim. 2:19-20; Jude 1:4; 1 Pet. 2:8.

3. *We reject* the teaching that God is unjust in choosing some sinners to salvation and leaving others to suffer merited condemnation.

8. The doctrine of this high mystery of predestination is to be handled with special prudence and care, that men attending the will of God revealed in His Word, and yielding obedience thereunto, may, from the certainty of their effectual vocation, be assured of their eternal election. So shall this doctrine afford matter of praise, reverence, and admiration of God, and of humility, diligence, and abundant consolation to all that sincerely obey the Gospel.
Rom. 9:20; Rom. 11:33; Deut. 29:29; 2 Pet. 1:10; Eph. 1:6; Rom. 11:33; Rom. 11:5-6, 20; 2 Pet. 1:10; Rom. 8:33; Luke 10:20.

Chapter 4: Of Creation

(Larger Catechism: 1, 15-17; Shorter Catechism: 1, 9-10)

1. It pleased God the Father, Son, and Holy Ghost, for the manifestation of the glory of His eternal power, wisdom, and goodness, in the beginning, to create, or make of nothing, the world, and all things therein whether visible or invisible, in the space of six days; and all very good.
Heb. 1:2; John 1:2-3; Gen. 1:2; Job 26:13; Job 33:4; Rom. 1:20; Jer. 10:12; Ps. 104:24; Ps. 33:5-6; Gen. 1; Heb. 11:3; Col. 1:16; Acts 17:24.

1. The account of creation in Genesis 1 and 2 is history, not mythology.
Heb. 11:3.

2. Since all things were created and exist according to the will of God they are controlled in purpose and duration by the same will.
Rev. 4:11; 2 Pet. 3:3-13.

2. After God had made all other creatures, He created man, male and female, with reasonable and immortal souls, endued with knowledge, righteousness, and true holiness, after His own image; having the law of God written in their hearts, and power to fulfil it: and yet under a possibility of transgressing, being left to the liberty of their own will, which was subject unto change. Beside this law written in their hearts, they received a command not to eat of the tree of the knowledge of good and evil, which while they kept, they were happy in their communion with God, and had dominion over the creatures.

3. The theory of evolution which assumes that chance happenings are an explanation of the origin and development of matter and living things is unscriptural. God created various kinds of living forms with tremendous potential for variation. The increase of varieties which has occurred is within genetic limitations provided at creation.
Gen. 1:11, 20, 27; Gen. 2:2.

4. *We deny* that man evolved from any lower form of life.
Gen. 2:7, 21-22.

Gen. 1:27; Gen. 2:7 with Eccl. 12:7, and Luke 23:43, and Matt. 10:28; Gen. 1:26; Col. 3:10; Eph. 4:24; Rom. 2:14-15; Eccl. 7:29; Gen. 3:6; Eccl. 7:29; Gen. 2:17; Gen. 3:8-11, 23; Gen. 1:26, 28.

5. *We reject* all theories of continuing creation. Gen. 2:2.

6. God created man and woman as His image bearers to complement one another. Scripture describes the responsibilities of each and their proper relationship to one another. Distinctions between the sexes do not imply superiority or inferiority of persons. Family life and social order become disrupted when these distinctions are confused or ignored. Gen. 2:20-24; Eph. 5:21-33; Rom. 1:26-27.

7. God made man ruler over His creation in a covenant relationship with Himself in order to glorify His name. As ruler, man was not created to be his own law-maker, but is subject to the covenant. Since the fall man continues to fulfill the creation mandate. Through Christ's redemptive reign over all things the gracious purposes of God for the whole creation are being accomplished through men, sinful though they are. Gen. 1:26-2:5; Gen. 3:17-19; Heb. 2:5-9; Eph. 1:20-23.

8. Man is steward of the creation and should treat his resources of material wealth, environment, health, energy and talents as gifts of God, for which he must give account. Gen. 1:26; Ps. 8:6; Gen. 2:15-17; Heb. 2:5-9; 1 Cor. 4:2; 1 Cor. 10:6, 11; 1 Pet. 4:10-11.

9. *We reject* any view of man's relationship to his environment which either leads to his irresponsible exploitation of, or denies his proper dominion over, the earth.

10. The whole creation now groans because of man's sin. It, along with man, will be delivered from corruption at the consummation of all things. Rom. 8:21-22.

Economics

11. The Scriptures teach that everything belongs to God; that the authority and power to obtain and use goods are given by God; and that men are to seek God's glory in the use of their goods. The Scriptures direct how goods are to be obtained and used. No existing economic system incorporates all these teachings. 1 Cor. 10:26; Deut. 8:18; 2 Chron. 1:12; Luke 12:13-21; Ps. 112; Acts 5:4; 1 Tim. 6:6-10, 17-19; Jas. 4:13.

12. *We reject* Marxist communism because of its doctrines of atheism, necessary class struggle, economic determinism, dialectical materialism, and the inherent illegitimacy of private property.

13. *We reject* that form of capitalism which holds that men

possess absolute property rights and that the state has no right to protect the weak and restrain evil in economic affairs.

14. *We reject* that form of socialism which denies the right to own property. We warn against the concentration of economic power in the hands of the state, as it tends to deprive men of the due reward of their labor.
Deut. 17:14-20; 1 Sam. 8:10-18.

15. The Scriptures require the Christian to exercise stewardship over his possessions. In view of that requirement, he should contribute gladly to the Lord's work and give generously to the poor and needy. Under the old covenant the Lord required the practice of tithing. Recognizing the greater blessings under the new covenant and the fact that Christ endorsed tithing, the Christian should respond out of love by giving at least as great a proportion of his income to the Lord's work through the Church.
Deut. 26:12-15; Mal. 3:10; Matt. 23:23.

16. The Church, regardless of the economic system under which it exists, has the duty to speak against social evils such as oppression of the poor. The Church must never become the instrument of any powerful exploiting class.
Amos 8:4-7; Isa. 5:8; Gal. 2:10; Prov. 14:21, 31; 1 John 3:17; Luke 18:22; Ps. 35:10; Ps. 41:1; Ps. 82:4.

17. To possess wealth is not in itself sinful, but men should resist the temptation to accumulate wealth by exploiting others or for sinful purposes.
Mic. 2:2; 1 Cor. 10:24; Eph. 4:28; 1 Tim. 6:6-10, 17-19.

Chapter 5: Of Providence

(Larger Catechism: 18-20, 141-142; Shorter Catechism: 11-12)

1. God the great Creator of all things doth uphold, direct, dispose, and govern all creatures, actions, and things, from the greatest even to the least, by His most wise and holy providence, according to His infallible fore-knowledge, and the free and immutable counsel of His own will, to the praise of the glory of His wisdom, power, justice, goodness and mercy.
Heb. 1:3; Dan. 4:34-35; Ps. 135:6; Acts 17:25-26, 28; Job 38—41; Matt. 10:29-31; Prov. 15:3; Ps. 104:24; Ps. 145:17; Acts 15:18; Ps. 94:8-11; Eph. 1:11; Ps. 33:10-11; Isa. 63:14; Eph. 3:10; Rom. 9:17; Gen. 45:7; Ps. 145:7.

1. *We reject* all theories of the continuation or dissolution of the universe due to any other cause than the will of the Creator.

2. God's providence should lead the believer to be patient in adversity and thankful in prosperity, resting confidently in his Lord. He is to seek to understand the meaning and purpose of God's dealings with him in the light of the Word of God.
Deut. 29:29; 1 Thess. 5:18; 2 Cor. 1:3-5; Amos 4:6-12.

2. Although, in relation to the fore-knowledge and decree of God, the first Cause, all things come to pass immutably, and infallibly: yet, by the same providence, He ordereth them to fall out, according to the nature of second causes, either necessarily, freely, or contingently.
Acts 2:23; Gen. 8:22; Jer. 31:35; Ex. 21:13 with Deut. 19:5; 1 Kings 22:28, 34; Isa. 10:6-7.

3. *We reject* the belief that God does not exercise His providence in all parts of His creation, and in all actions of His creatures; or that some areas of life are controlled by so-called luck or chance.
Amos 3:6.

3. God in His ordinary providence maketh use of means, yet is free to work without, above, and against them at His pleasure.
Acts 27:31, 44; Isa. 55:10-11; Hos. 2:21-22; Hos. 1:7; Matt. 4:4; Job 34:20; Rom. 4:19-21; 2 Kings 6:6; Dan. 3:27.

4. Gambling is a sin against God because it denies His providential care and increases dependence on the erroneous notion of luck or chance. It involves and encourages greed and the desire to get something for nothing at the expense of others. Its satanic character is demonstrated in the way it obsesses individuals. Some examples of unwarranted gambling the Christian should avoid are lotteries, bingo for gain, wagerings, raffles and bets. Many of the same objections may be brought against sweepstakes, door prizes, drawings and other similar practices. The Church should testify against the dependence of public agencies on revenues derived from gambling sources.
2 Thess. 3:9-10; Prov. 15:27; Prov. 16:33; Ex. 20:15, 17; 1 Tim. 6:9-11.

4. The almighty power, unsearchable wisdom, and infinite goodness of God so far manifest themselves in His providence, that it extendeth itself even to the first fall, and all other sins of angels and men; and that not by a bare permission, but such as hath joined with it a most wise and powerful bounding, and otherwise ordering and governing of them, in a manifold dispensation, to His own holy ends; yet so, as the sinfulness thereof proceedeth only from the creature, and not from God, who, being most holy and righteous, neither is, nor can be, the author or approver of sin.
Rom. 11:32-34; 2 Sam. 24:1 with 1 Chron. 21:1; 1 Kings 22:22-23; 1 Chron. 10:4, 13-14; 2 Sam. 16:10; Acts 2:23; Acts 4:27-28; Acts 14:16; Ps. 76:10; 2 Kings 19:28; Gen. 50:20; Isa. 10:6-7, 12; Jas. 1:13-14, 17; 1 John 2:16; Ps. 50:21.

5. The most wise, righteous, and gracious God doth oftentimes leave for a season His own children to manifold temptations, and the corruption of their own hearts, to chastise them for their former sins, or to discover unto them the hidden strength of corruption, and deceitfulness of their hearts, that they may be humbled; and, to raise them to a more close and constant dependence for their support upon Himself, and to make them more watchful against all future occasions of sin, and for sundry other just and holy ends.
2 Chron. 32:25-26, 31; 2 Sam. 24:1; 2 Cor. 12:7-9; Ps. 73; Ps. 77:1-12; Mark 14:66-72 with John 21:15-17.

6. As for those wicked and ungodly men whom God, as a righteous Judge, for former sins doth blind and harden, from

them He not only withholdeth His grace, whereby they might have been enlightened in their understandings, and wrought upon in their hearts; but sometimes also withdraweth the gifts which they had, and exposeth them to such objects as their corruption makes occasions of sin; and, withal, gives them over to their own lusts, the temptations of the world, and the power of Satan: whereby it comes to pass that they harden themselves, even under those means which God useth for the softening of others.
Rom. 1:24, 26, 28; Rom. 11:7-8; Deut. 29:4; Matt. 13:12; Matt. 25:29; Deut. 2:30; 2 Kings 8:12-13; Ps. 81:11-12; 2 Thess. 2:10-12; Ex. 7:3 with Ex. 8:15, 32; 2 Cor. 2:15-16; Isa. 8:14; 1 Pet. 2:7-8; Isa. 6:9-10 with Acts 28:26-27.

7. As the providence of God doth in general reach to all creatures, so after a most special manner it taketh care of His Church, and disposeth all things to the good thereof.
1 Tim. 4:10; Amos 9:8-9; Rom. 8:28; Isa. 43:3-5, 14.

5. Satan has power in the world which includes predictions of the future, signs and wonders that deceive, and possession of persons. Satan often duplicates that which belongs to God even to the establishment of churches that serve him. Therefore Christians are to flee the working of Satan in such things as fortune telling, horoscopes, astrology, palmistry, witchcraft, conjurings, seances, drug experiences and Satan worship.
2 Kings 23:24; Acts 16:16; Eph. 6:12; Lev. 20:27; 1 Pet. 5:8-9; Dan. 4:7; Isa. 47:12-15; Deut. 18:10-14; 2 Thess. 2:8-10; Rev. 2:11.

Chapter 6
Of the Fall of Man, of Sin, and of the Punishment Thereof

(Larger Catechism: 21-29; 149-152; Shorter Catechism: 13-19; 82-84)

1. Our first parents, being seduced by the subtilty and temptation of Satan, sinned in eating the forbidden fruit. This their sin God was pleased, according to His wise and holy counsel, to permit, having purposed to order it to His own glory.
Gen. 3:13; 2 Cor. 11:3; Rom. 11:32.

2. By this sin they fell from their original righteousness and communion with God, and so became dead in sin, and wholly defiled in all the faculties and parts of soul and body.
Gen. 3:6-8; Eccl. 7:29; Rom. 3:23; Gen. 2:17; Eph. 2:1; Titus 1:15; Gen. 6:5; Jer. 17:9; Rom. 3:10-19.

3. They being the root of all mankind, the guilt of this sin was imputed, and the same death in sin and corrupted nature conveyed, to all their posterity descending from them by ordinary generation.
Gen. 1:27-28, and Gen. 2:16-17, and Acts 17:26 with Rom. 5:12, 15-19, and 1 Cor. 15:21-22, 49; Ps. 51:5; Gen. 5:3; Job 14:4; Job 15:14.

4. From this original corruption, whereby we are utterly indisposed, disabled, and made opposite to all good, and wholly inclined to all evil, do proceed all actual transgressions.
Rom. 5:6; Rom. 8:7; Rom. 7:18; Col. 1:21; Gen. 6:5; Gen. 8:21; Rom. 3:10-12; Jas. 1:14-15; Eph. 2:2-3; Matt. 15:19.

1. This corruption of man's nature is commonly called total depravity. Two examples in the Scripture demonstrate that being human is not equivalent to being sinful—that of Adam before the fall and of Christ in His human nature. Since the fall every part of man's nature is affected by sin. His under-

standing is darkened; he is motivated by wrong principles, is rebellious and wholly unable of his own will to love God or to obtain salvation. Natural men are not equally evil, nor as evil as they might be. They may conform to some human standards of goodness.
Heb. 4:15; Gen. 6:5; Rom. 5:12-17; Rom. 8:7; Rom. 3:23; Rom. 7:18; Eph. 4:18; Gen. 3:22; Mark 10:20.

5. This corruption of nature, during this life, doth remain in those that are regenerated; and although it be, through Christ, pardoned and mortified, yet both itself and all the motions thereof are truly and properly sin.
1 John 1:8, 10; Rom. 7:14, 17-18, 23; Jas. 3:2; Prov. 20:9; Eccl. 7:20; Rom. 7:5, 7-8, 25; Gal. 5:17.

6. Every sin, both original and actual, being a transgression of the righteous law of God, and contrary thereunto, doth, in its own nature, bring guilt upon the sinner; whereby he is bound over to the wrath of God, and curse of the law, and so made subject to death, with all miseries spiritual, temporal, and eternal.
1 John 3:4; Rom. 2:15; Rom. 3:9, 19; Eph. 2:3; Gal. 3:10; Rom. 6:23; Eph. 4:18; Rom. 8:20; Lam. 3:39; Matt. 25:41; 2 Thess. 1:9.

2. Every man was created in the image of God. His life, therefore, whether he is regenerate or unregenerate, should be recognized as having value to himself, to society, and to God.
Prov. 16:4; Gen. 9:5-6; Matt. 10:29-31; Gen. 1:27; Rom. 5:7-8; Acts 17:24-29; Rom. 9:20-24.

Chapter 7: Of God's Covenant with Man

(Larger Catechism: 30-36; Shorter Catechism: 16-20)

1. The distance between God and the creature is so great, that although reasonable creatures do owe obedience unto Him as their Creator, yet they could never have any fruition of Him as their blessedness and reward, but by some voluntary condescension on God's part, which He hath been pleased to express by way of covenant.
Isa. 40:13-17; Job 9:32-33; 1 Sam. 2:25; Ps. 113:5-6; Ps. 100:2-3; Job 22:2-3; Job 35:7-8; Luke 17:10; Acts 17:24-25.

2. The first covenant made with man was a covenant of works, wherein life was promised to Adam, and in him to his posterity, upon condition of perfect and personal obedience.
Gal. 3:12; Rom. 10:5; Rom. 5:12-20; Gen. 2:17; Gal. 3:10.

3. Man by his fall, having made himself incapable of life by that covenant, the Lord was pleased to make a second, commonly called the covenant of grace; wherein He freely offereth unto sinners life and salvation by Jesus Christ, requiring of them faith in Him that they may be saved, and promising to give unto all those that are ordained unto life His Holy Spirit, to

1. *We reject* the teaching that Adam was not a covenant head and representative of all his descendants. *We reject* the view that Adam's headship involves any injustice.

2. By this principle of covenant headship the guilt and penalty of sin come upon all men by Adam's one sin; and by the obedience of Christ, the second covenant head, righteousness and life come upon all men who believe.
Rom. 5:12-21.

3. The Covenant of Works has not been revoked. All men

make them willing and able to believe.
Gal. 3:21; Rom. 8:3; Rom. 3:20-21; Gen. 3:15; Isa. 42:6; Mark 16:15-16; John 3:16; Rom. 10:6, 9; Gal. 3:11; Ezek. 36:26-27; John 6:44-45.

remain under its requirement of perfect obedience and will have to give account according to it at the last judgment. In the Covenant of Grace Jesus Christ has fulfilled the requirements of the Covenant of Works for His people. By His death Christ secured the delay of the full penalty of death for sin (the second death, Rev. 20:14-15) for all men. They therefore may enjoy the creation and have some fruitful toil in it for God's glory, even though they be rebellious against Him. This is usually called common grace.
Heb. 12:14; 2 Cor. 5:10, 21; Col. 1:16-20; 1 Cor. 8:6; Gen. 4:20-24; Ps. 76:10.

4. This covenant of grace is frequently set forth in Scripture by the name of a Testament, in reference to the death of Jesus Christ the Testator, and to the everlasting inheritance, with all things belonging to it, therein bequeathed.
Heb. 9:15-17; Heb. 7:22; Luke 22:20; 1 Cor. 11:25.

5. This covenant was differently administered in the time of the law, and in the time of the gospel: under the law, it was administered by promises, prophecies, sacrifices, circumcision, the paschal lamb, and other types and ordinances delivered to the people of the Jews, all fore-signifying Christ to come: which were, for that time, sufficient and efficacious, through the operation of the Spirit, to instruct and build up the elect in faith in the promised Messiah, by whom they had full remission of sins, and eternal salvation; and is called, the Old Testament.
2 Cor. 3:6-9; Heb. 8—10; Rom. 4:11; Col. 2:11-12; 1 Cor. 5:7; 1 Cor. 10:1-4; Heb. 11:13; John 8:56; Gal. 3:7-9, 14.

4. *We reject* the concept that God extends grace to any man apart from the atoning work of Christ.
Isa. 45:1-4 with Rom. 3:21-26; Acts 17:30-31.

5. By the Covenant of Grace, God brings the elect into fellowship with Himself. This fellowship begins in this life when man repents and believes in Jesus Christ; it is a fuller fellowship when at death men depart to be with Christ; and it will be made perfect when believers shall be raised up in glory.
1 Thess. 4:16-17; 1 Cor. 15:52.

6. Under the gospel, when Christ, the substance, was exhibited, the ordinances in which this covenant is dispensed are the preaching of the Word, and the administration of the sacraments of Baptism and the Lord's Supper: which, though fewer in number, and administered with more simplicity, and less outward glory; yet, in them, it is held forth in more fulness, evidence, and spiritual efficacy, to all nations, both Jews and Gentiles; and is called the New Testament. There are not therefore two covenants of grace, differing in substance, but one and the same, under various dispensations.
Col. 2:17; Matt. 28:19-20; 1 Cor. 11:23-25; Heb. 12:22-28; Jer. 31:33-34; Matt. 28:19; Eph. 2:15-19; Luke 22:20; Gal. 3:14, 16; Rom. 3:21-23, 30; Ps. 32:1 with Rom. 4:3, 6, 16-17, 23-24; Heb. 13:8; Acts 15:11.

6. *We reject* the teaching that God will reinstate the temple and its rites and ceremonies.
Heb. 9:1-10, 28.

7. *We reject* the teaching that salvation is or has been available in any way other than by the grace offered and confirmed in Christ.
Rom. 3:20-26; Acts 4:12.

Chapter 8: Of Christ the Mediator

(Larger Catechism: 32-55, 57; Shorter Catechism: 21-28)

1. It pleased God, in His eternal purpose, to choose and ordain the Lord Jesus, His only begotten Son, to be the Mediator between God and man; the Prophet, Priest, and King, the Head and Saviour of His Church, the Heir of all things, and Judge of the world: unto whom He did from all eternity give a people, to be His seed, and to be by Him in time redeemed, called, justified, sanctified, and glorified.
Isa. 42:1; 1 Pet. 1:19-20; John 3:16; 1 Tim. 2:5; Acts 3:22; Heb. 5: 5-6; Ps. 2:6; Luke 1:33; Eph. 5:23; Heb. 1:2; Acts 17:31; John 17: 6; Ps. 22:30; Isa. 53:10; 1 Tim. 2:6; Isa. 55:4-5; 1 Cor. 1:30.

2. The Son of God, the second person in the Trinity, being very and eternal God, of one substance and equal with the Father, did, when the fulness of time was come, take upon Him man's nature, with all the essential properties and common infirmities thereof, yet without sin; being conceived by the power of the Holy Ghost, in the womb of the virgin Mary, of her substance. So that two whole, perfect, and distinct natures, the Godhead and the manhood, were inseparably joined together in one person, without conversion, compostition, or confusion. Which person is very God, and very man, yet one Christ, the only Mediator between God and man.
John 1:1, 14; 1 John 5:20; Phil. 2:6; Gal. 4:4; Heb 2:14, 16-17; Heb. 4:15; Luke 1:27, 31, 35; Gal 4:4; Luke 1:35; Col. 2:9; Rom. 9:5; 1 Pet. 3:18; 1 Tim. 3:16; Rom. 1:3-4; 1 Tim. 2:5.

3. The Lord Jesus, in His human nature thus united to the divine, was sanctified and anointed with the Holy Spirit, above measure, having in Him all the treasures of wisdom and knowledge; in whom it pleased the Father that all fulness should dwell; to the end that, being holy, harmless, undefiled, and full of grace and truth, He might be thoroughly furnished to execute the office of a Mediator and Surety. Which office He took not unto Himself, but was thereunto called by His Father, who put all power and judgment into His hand, and gave Him commandment to execute the same.
Ps. 45:7; John 3:34; Col. 2:3; Col. 1:19; Heb. 7:26; John 1:14; Acts 10:38; Heb. 12:24; Heb. 7:22; Heb. 5:4-5; John 5:22, 27; Matt. 28:18; Acts 2:36.

4. This office the Lord Jesus did most willingly undertake; which that He might discharge, He was made under the law, and did perfectly fulfil it, endured most grievous torments immediately in His soul, and most painful sufferings in His body; was crucified, and died; was buried, and remained under the power of death; yet saw no corruption. On the third day He arose from the dead, with the same body in which He suffered, with which also He ascended into heaven, and there

1. Jesus Christ, as Mediator, governs all creatures and all their actions for His own glory. Submission is due to Him from all men and angels. All men, in every possible relation and condition, are under obligation to promote His gracious purposes according to His law. The holy angels minister, under His direction, to the heirs of salvation.
Eph. 1:20-22; Heb. 2:8; Phil. 2:9-11; Ps. 2; Heb. 1:4.

2. Jesus Christ, as Head over all things for the sake of the Church, rules in perfect wisdom and justice over all parts of His creation including wicked men and devils. He makes them, and all their counsels and efforts, serve God's glory in the plan of redemption.
Rom. 8:28; Eph. 1:22-23; John 17:1-5; Luke 9:26.

3. *We reject* any teaching that denies or obscures the truth that Jesus is both God and man in two distinct natures and one person forever.

4. *We reject* any teaching that would place any mediator between Christ and man.

5. It is in the office of Mediator that Christ fulfills and applies the Covenant of Grace, and in doing so, accomplishes the Covenant of Works.
Heb. 1:3; Heb. 2:5-9; Col. 1:16-20; Rev. 21:24-27.

sitteth at the right hand of His Father, making intercession, and shall return to judge men and angels at the end of the world.
Ps. 40:7-8 with Heb. 10:5-10; John 10:18; Phil. 2:8; Gal. 4:4; Matt. 3:15; Matt. 5:17; Matt. 26:37-38; Luke 22:44; Matt. 27: 46; Matt. 26—27; Phil. 2:8; Acts 2:23-24, 27; Acts 13:37; Rom. 6:9; 1 Cor. 15:3-4; John 20:25, 27; Mark 16:19; Rom. 8:34; Heb. 9:24; Heb. 7:25; Rom. 14:9-10; Acts 1:11; Acts 10:42; Matt. 13: 40-42; Jude 6; 2 Pet. 2:4.

5. The Lord Jesus, by His perfect obedience, and sacrifice of Himself, which He, through the eternal Spirit, once offered up unto God, hath fully satisfied the justice of His Father; and purchased, not only reconciliation, but an everlasting inheritance in the kingdom of heaven, for all those whom the Father hath given unto Him.
Rom. 5:19; Heb. 9:14, 16; Heb 10:14; Eph. 5:2; Rom. 3:25-26; Dan. 9:24, 26; Col. 1:19-20; Eph. 1:11, 14; John 17:2; Heb. 9:12, 15.

6. We reject the teaching that all men already are in Christ and have been redeemed by Him, whether they realize it or not.

7. Christ did not lay down His life to atone for the sins of all mankind, nor for an indefinite number of sinners. His sacrifice was indeed sufficient to save the whole world, had it been designed to do so; but in the purpose of God and in the undertaking of Christ, it was determined that He should make atonement for those who were elected in Him to everlasting life; these only He represented, and these only shall be saved through His redemption. This truth is commonly called limited atonement or particular redemption.
John 10:14-15, 25-30; John 3:16; Acts 20:28; Rev. 5:9; John 17:9-10.

6. Although the work of redemption was not actually wrought by Christ till after His incarnation, yet the virtue, efficacy, and benefits thereof were communicated unto the elect in all ages successively from the beginning of the world, in and by those promises, types, and sacrifices, wherein He was revealed, and signified to be the seed of the woman which should bruise the serpent's head; and the Lamb slain from the beginning of the world: being yesterday and today the same, and for ever.
Gal. 4:4-5; Gen. 3:15; Rev. 13:8; Heb. 13:8.

7. Christ, in the work of mediation, acteth according to both natures, by each nature doing that which is proper to itself: yet, by reason of the unity of the person, that which is proper to one nature, is sometimes in Scripture attributed to the person denominated by the other nature.
Heb. 9:14; 1 Pet. 3:18; Acts 20:28; John 3:13; 1 John 3:16.

8. To all those for whom Christ hath purchased redemption, He doth certainly and effectually apply and communicate the same, making intercession for them, and revealing unto them, in and by the Word, the mysteries of salvation, effectually persuading them by His Spirit to believe and obey, and governing their hearts by His Word and Spirit, overcoming all their enemies by His almighty power and wisdom, in such manner, and ways, as are most consonant to His wonderful and unsearchable dispensation.
John 6:37, 39; John 10:15-16; 1 John 2:1-2; Rom. 8:34; John 15: 13, 15; Eph. 1:7-9; John 17:6; John 14:26; Heb. 12:2; 2 Cor. 4:13; Rom. 8:9, 14; Rom. 15:18-19; John 17:17; Ps. 110:1; 1 Cor. 15: 25-26; Mal. 4:2-3; Col. 2:15.

8. The reprobate, because of their connection with God's elect who live among them, are partakers of some benefits which flow from Christ's death; divine judgments are sometimes averted for the sake of the saints; the peace and prosperity of nations are furthered by the providence of God over His people; benevolence and temperance are promoted by the Church's teaching and influence; and the world is continued under its present administration until all the elect are brought to salvation.
Isa. 45:1-4; Matt. 5:13-14; Matt. 13:29; Isa. 65:8; Matt. 24:22; Jer. 29:7; Gen. 39:5; Gal. 6:10; Gen. 18:26; Ps. 75:3; Gen. 9:11.

Chapter 9: Of Free Will

1. God *hath* endued the will of man with that natural liberty, that it is neither forced, nor by any absolute necessity of nature determined to good or evil.
Matt. 17:12; Jas. 1:14; Deut. 30:19.

2. Man, in his state of innocency, had freedom and power to will and to do that which was good, and well pleasing to God; but yet mutably, so that he might fall from it. Eccl. 7:29; Gen. 1:26; Gen. 2:16-17; Gen. 3:6.

3. Man, by his fall into a state of sin, hath wholly lost all ability of will to any spiritual good accompanying salvation: so as, a natural man, being altogether averse from that good, and dead in sin, is not able, by his own strength, to convert himself, or to prepare himself thereunto.
Rom. 5:6; Rom. 8:7; John 15:5; Rom. 3:10, 12; Eph. 2:1, 5; Col. 2:13; John 6:44, 65; Eph. 2:2-5; 1 Cor. 2:14; Titus 3:3-5.

4. When God converts a sinner, and translates him into the state of grace, He freeth him from his natural bondage under sin; and, by His grace alone, enables him freely to will and to do that which is spiritually good; yet so, as that by reason of his remaining corruption, he doth not perfectly, nor only, will that which is good, but doth also will that which is evil.
Col. 1:13; John 8:34, 36; Phil. 2:13; Rom. 6:18, 22; Gal. 5:17; Rom. 7:15, 18-19, 21, 23.

1. *We reject* the teaching that the work of the Holy Spirit in regeneration is dependent upon the exercise of man's free will.

5. The will of man is made perfectly and immutably free to good alone, in the state of glory only.
Eph. 4:13; Heb. 12:23; 1 John 3:2; Jude 24.

Chapter 10: Of Effectual Calling

(Larger Catechism: 66-68; Shorter Catechism: 31-32)

1. Preaching the Gospel consists in the offer of salvation through Christ to sinners, accompanied with such an explanation of the various parts of God's Word as may help to persuade men to receive Christ as Savior, and to live and walk in Him.
2 Cor. 5:20; Matt. 28:20; Isa. 55:1-3.

1. All those whom God hath predestinated unto life, and those only, He is pleased in His appointed and accepted time effectually to call, by His Word and Spirit, out of that state of sin and death, in which they are by nature, to grace and salvation by Jesus Christ; enlightening their minds spiritually and savingly to understand the things of God; taking away their heart of stone, and giving unto them a heart of flesh;

2. The elect are effectually called by means of the Gospel offer. This offer is not a declaration to any sinner that his name is in the Book of Life. It is founded upon God's command to offer Christ and all His benefits to sinners. There is no inconsistency between the biblical doctrine of particular redemption and the command to offer the Gospel to all men.
Deut. 29:29; Mark 16:15; Luke 24:46-47; 2 Tim. 2:19.

renewing their wills, and by His almighty power determining them to that which is good, and effectually drawing them to Jesus Christ: yet so, as they come most freely, being made willing by His grace.
Rom. 8:30; Rom. 11:7; Eph. 1:10-11; 2 Thess. 2:13-14; 2 Cor. 3: 3, 6; Rom. 8:2; Eph. 2:1-5; 2 Tim. 1:9-10; Acts 26:18; 1 Cor. 2: 10, 12; Eph. 1:17-18; Ezek. 36:26; Ezek. 11:19; Phil. 2:13; Deut. 30:6; Ezek. 36:27; Eph. 1:19; John 6:44-45; Song of Sol. 1:4; Ps. 110:3; John 6:37; Rom. 6:16-18.

2. This effectual call is of God's free and special grace alone, not from anything at all foreseen in man, who is altogether passive therein, until being quickened and renewed by the Holy Spirit, he is thereby enabled to answer this call, and to embrace the grace offered and conveyed in it.
2 Tim. 1:9; Titus 3:4-5; Eph. 2:4-5, 8-9; Rom. 9:11; 1 Cor. 2:14; Rom. 8:7; Eph. 2:5; John 6:37; Ezek. 36:27; John 5:25.

3. Elect infants, dying in infancy, are regenerated, and saved by Christ through the Spirit, who worketh when, and where, and how He pleaseth: so also, are all other elect persons who are uncapable of being outwardly called by the ministry of the Word.
Luke 18:15-16, and Acts 2:38-39, and John 3:3, 5, and 1 John 5: 12, and Rom. 8:9 compared; John 3:8; 1 John 5:12; Acts 4:12.

4. Others, not elected, although they may be called by the ministry of the Word, and may have some common operations of the Spirit, yet they never truly come unto Christ, and therefore cannot be saved: much less can men, not professing the Christian religion, be saved in any other way whatsoever, be they never so diligent to frame their lives according to the light of nature, and the law of that religion they do profess. And, to assert and maintain that they may, is very pernicious, and to be detested.
Matt. 22:14; Matt. 7:22; Matt. 13:20-21; Heb. 6:4-5; John 6: 64-66; John 8:24; Acts 4:12; John 14:6; Eph. 2:12; John 4:22; John 17:3; 2 John 9-11; 1 Cor. 16:22; Gal. 1:6-8.

3. *We reject* the teaching that the Gospel offer of salvation is freely and truly offered only to the elect. *We reject* the teaching that particular redemption is to be so understood and presented that Christ as ransom and propitiation is not preached or offered to all men indiscriminately.

4. *We reject* the teaching that all will be effectually called and ultimately saved.

5. *We reject* the view that those who are diligent and sincere in a false religion have eternal life.

6. Evangelism is the proclamation of Jesus Christ as Savior and Lord as He is offered in the Gospel. Christ laid the responsibility upon the whole Church to make this proclamation. The task is not restricted to ordained officers. Each member is to take his share of the responsibility according to the gifts God has given him.
Acts 2:36; Matt. 28:18-20; John 20:21; 1 Cor. 12:4-11; Eph. 4: 7-16.

7. Those evangelizing should use all available means consistent with the Bible so that every person may be given the opportunity to hear, understand and receive the Gospel. While guarding against undue pressure, we must urge men to be reconciled to God.
1 Cor. 9:20-22; 1 Cor. 2:2-5; 2 Cor. 5:20.

8. Evangelism is not only to seek the conversion of sinners but also to build them up to become effective in the Church's continuing task.
Col. 1:27-28; Eph. 4:12-15.

9. The Great Commission requires the Church to take the whole Gospel to the whole world. The Bible recognizes the legitimacy of diverse cultures. Every culture is to be transformed and made subject to Christ through redeemed men, all for the glory of God.
Matt. 28:18-20; 1 Cor. 9:19-23; 1 Cor. 10:32-33; Rev. 21:24, 26; Ps. 72:10-11.

10. Wherever consistent with faithfulness to God's truth, different branches of the visible church should cooperate in evangelism to strengthen their witness by demonstrating their unity in Christ.
John 17:20-21.

Chapter 11: Of Justification

(Larger Catechism: 70-73, 77; Shorter Catechism: 32-33, 36)

1. Those whom God effectually calleth, He also freely justifieth: not by infusing righteousness into them, but by pardoning their sins, and by accounting and accepting their persons as righteous, not for anything wrought in them, or done by them, but for Christ's sake alone; nor by imputing faith itself, the act of believing, or any other evangelical obedience to them, as their righteousness, but by imputing the obedience and satisfaction of Christ unto them, they receiving and resting on Him and His righteousness by faith; which faith they have not of themselves, it is the gift of God.
Rom. 8:30; Rom. 3:24; Rom. 4:5-8; 2 Cor. 5:19, 21; Rom. 3: 22, 24-25, 27-28; Titus 3:5, 7; Eph. 1:7; Jer. 23:6; 1 Cor. 1:30-31; Rom. 5:17-19; Acts 10:43; Gal. 2:16; Phil. 3:9; Acts 13:38-39; Eph. 2:7-8.

1. Justification is a legal declaration that the sinner is acquitted from the guilt of sin, and is considered righteous before God. Although he is still an unworthy sinner, yet because he is united to Christ, he has Christ's perfect righteousness imputed to him.

2. Faith, thus receiving and resting on Christ, and His righteousness, is the alone instrument of justification; yet it is not alone in the person justified, but is ever accompanied with all other saving graces, and is no dead faith, but worketh by love.
John 1:12; Rom. 3:28; Rom. 5:1; Jas. 2:17, 22, 26; Gal. 5:6.

2. Faith in Christ is the only means of justification. The imputed righteousness of Christ is the only basis for justification.

3. *We reject* the teaching that man's works have a part in his justification.

3. Christ, by His obedience and death, did fully discharge the debt of all those that are thus justified, and did make a proper, real, and full satisfaction to His Father's justice in their behalf. Yet, inasmuch as He was given by the Father for them; and His obedience and satisfaction accepted in their stead; and both freely, not for anything in them; their justification is

4. The justification of the believer does not diminish his

only of free grace; that both the exact justice, and rich grace of God, might be glorified in the justification of sinners.
Rom. 5:8-10, 19; 1 Tim. 2:5-6; Heb. 10:10, 14; Dan. 9:24, 26; Isa. 53:4-6, 10-12; Rom. 8:32; 2 Cor. 5:21; Matt. 3:17; Eph. 5:2; Rom. 3:24; Eph. 1:7; Rom. 3:26; Eph. 2:7.

obligation to obey divine law.
Eccl. 12:13; 1 Cor. 9:21; Rom. 6:1, 12-23; Rom. 3:21.

4. God did, from all eternity, decree to justify all the elect, and Christ did, in the fulness of time, die for their sins, and rise again for their justification: nevertheless, they are not justified, until the Holy Spirit doth, in due time, actually apply Christ unto them.
Gal. 3:8; 1 Pet. 1:2, 19-20; Rom. 8:30; Gal. 4:4; 1 Tim. 2:6; Rom. 4:25; Col. 1:21-22; Gal 2:16; Titus 3:3-7.

5. God doth continue to forgive the sins of those that are justified; and, although they can never fall from the state of justification; yet they may, by their sins, fall under God's fatherly displeasure, and not have the light of His countenance restored unto them, until they humble themselves, confess their sins, beg pardon, and renew their faith and repentance.
Matt. 6:12; 1 John 1:7, 9; 1 John 2:1-2; Luke 22:32; John 10:28; Heb. 10:14; Ps. 89:31-33; Ps. 51:7-12; Ps. 32:5; Matt. 26:75; 1 Cor. 11:30, 32; Luke 1:20.

6. The justification of believers under the old testament was, in all these respects, one and the same with the justification of believers under the new testament.
Gal. 3:9, 13-14; Rom. 4:22-24; Heb. 13:8.

Chapter 12: Of Adoption

(Larger Catechism: 74; Shorter Catechism: 32, 34, 36)

1. All those that are justified, God vouchsafeth, in and for His only Son Jesus Christ, to make partakers of the grace of adoption: by which they are taken into the number, and enjoy the liberties and privileges of the children of God, have His name put upon them, receive the spirit of adoption, have access to the throne of grace with boldness, are enabled to cry, Abba, Father, are pitied, protected, provided for, and chastened by Him as by a father; yet never cast off, but sealed to the day of redemption, and inherit the promises, as heirs of everlasting salvation.
Eph. 1:5; Gal. 4:4-5; Rom. 8:17; John 1:12; Jer. 14:9; 2 Cor. 6:18; Rev. 3:12; Rom. 8:15; Eph. 3:12; Rom. 5:2; Gal. 4:6; Ps. 103:13; Prov. 14:26; Matt. 6:30, 32; 1 Pet. 5:7; Heb. 12:6; Lam. 3:31; Eph. 4:30; Heb. 6:12; 1 Pet. 1:3-4; Heb. 1:14.

1. All the elect, and only they, are adopted into the family of God. The adoption of saints under the Old Testament dispensation was as real as that under the New Testament, although they were regarded as children under age. Under the New Testament God bestows His Spirit more abundantly. He gives more knowledge of, and intimacy with, Himself. He receives on equal grounds those from every part of the world. He allows greater boldness in approaching Him.
Eph. 1:5; Gal. 3:9; Heb. 13:9-10; Rom. 9:4; Jer. 3:4; Gal. 4:1-5; Matt. 11:11; 2 Cor. 3:10-18; Rom. 9:26; Ps. 72:17.

2. Justification and adoption, although inseparably connected, are nevertheless distinct from one another. They are both acts of God's free grace. They are both performed once, and not repeated. They both spring from the grace of God; both give a right to all the privileges of the sons of God; and both are received through faith alone.
John 1:12; Titus 3:7; 1 John 3:1; Jer. 3:19; Gal. 3:26; Rom. 8:15-17.

3. Justification applies to believers as those who were guilty, and in a state of condemnation, but whose sins are now pardoned, and they are accounted righteous. Adoption applies to believers as those who were aliens and strangers to God. They were children of wrath, but by this gracious act are brought near unto God and made the children of God and joint heirs with Jesus Christ.
Eph. 2:2-3; 2 Cor. 6:17-18; 1 Pet. 5:7; Heb. 12:28; Rom. 8:17; Ps. 16:5; Eph. 1:7; Gal. 4:7.

4. There is a sense in which God is the Father of all men, because He created them. They are therefore obligated to love and seek the welfare of one another; yet to the redeemed alone belongs the right to be called the sons of God.
Acts 17:29; Matt. 5:44-45; John 1:12; 1 John 3:1; Rom. 8:14.

5. *We reject* the common conception of the universal fatherhood of God and the universal brotherhood of men, which denies the distinction between the saved and the unsaved.
1 John 2:23; John 8:44.

6. *We reject* the teaching that sonship, conferred in adoption, will ever be annulled by God.

Chapter 13: Of Sanctification

(Larger Catechism: 75-78; Shorter Catechism: 32, 35-36)

1. God's work of sanctification is designed to restore the whole person after the image of God. The moral law of God, perfectly fulfilled in the life of Christ, reveals God's holiness and declares His will to man, and is therefore the standard for sanctification.
Rom. 8:29; 1 Thess. 5:23-24.

1. They who are effectually called and regenerated, having a new heart and a new spirit created in them, are further sanctified, really and personally, through the virtue of Christ's death and resurrection, by His Word and Spirit dwelling in them: the dominion of the whole body of sin is destroyed, and the several lusts thereof are more and more weakened and mortified; and they more and more quickened and strengthened in all saving graces, to the practice of true holiness, without which no man shall see the Lord.
1 Cor. 6:11; Acts 20:32; Phil. 3:10; Rom. 6:5-6; John 17:17; Eph. 5:26; 2 Thess. 2:13; Rom. 6:6, 14; Gal. 5:24; Rom. 8:13; Col. 1: 11; Eph. 3:16-19; 2 Cor. 7:1; Heb. 12:14.

2. This sanctification is throughout, in the whole man; yet imperfect in this life, there abiding still some remnants of corruption in every part: whence ariseth a continual and ir-

2. *We reject* the view that in this life some Christians do not sin.
1 John 1:9; 1 Tim. 1:15.

reconcilable war; the flesh lusting against the Spirit, and the Spirit against the flesh.
1 Thess. 5:23; 1 John 1:10; Rom. 7:18, 23; Phil. 3:12; Gal. 5:17; 1 Pet. 2:11.

3. Proper proclamation of the doctrine of sanctification must call believers to struggle diligently against sin.
Phil. 2:12-13; 2 Cor. 7:1; Eph. 6:10-18; Heb. 12:4.

3. In which war, although the remaining corruption, for a time, may much prevail; yet through the continual supply of strength from the sanctifying Spirit of Christ, the regenerate part doth overcome; and so, the saints grow in grace, perfecting holiness in the fear of God.
Rom. 7:23; Rom. 6:14; 1 John 5:4; Eph. 4:15-16; 2 Pet. 3:18; 2 Cor. 3:18; 2 Cor. 7:1.

4. Sanctification is inseparably connected with justification, but is distinct from it. By justification the sinner is acquitted from condemnation; by sanctification he is made holy, and prepared for the happiness of heaven. Justification is complete at once, and equal in all believers; sanctification is neither equal in all, nor perfect in any, while in this life. Nevertheless, all who are justified shall be completely sanctified.
2 Cor. 5:17; Rom. 8:1-2; 2 Thess. 2:13; Rom 7:19, 21; Phil. 1:6; Heb. 12:23; Eph. 5:27; 1 Thess. 5:23-24.

Chapter 14: Of Saving Faith

(Larger Catechism: 60, 72-73; Shorter Catechism: 29-30)

1. Saving faith is the gift of the triune God. It is the Father's will that the elect should be united to Christ by faith. The Son, by His death, provided that saving faith should be freely granted to them. The Holy Spirit, therefore, regenerates each one of them, enabling them to receive Jesus Christ by faith as their Lord and Savior.
Rom. 3:25-26; Rom. 1:16-17; Col. 2:12; Phil. 1:29; 2 Thess. 2:13; 1 Pet. 1:3; Eph. 1:3-14; Rom. 8:28-29.

2. *We reject* the teaching that regeneration is the result of saving faith.

1. The grace of faith, whereby the elect are enabled to believe to the saving of their souls, is the work of the Spirit of Christ in their hearts; and is ordinarily wrought by the ministry of the Word: by which also, and by the administration of the sacraments, and prayer, it is increased and strengthened.
Heb. 10:39; 2 Cor. 4:13; Eph. 1:17-19; Eph. 2:8; Rom. 10:14, 17; 1 Pet. 2:2; Acts 20:32; Rom. 4:11; Luke 17:5; Rom. 1:16-17.

2. By this faith, a Christian believeth to be true whatsoever is revealed in the Word, for the authority of God Himself speaking therein; and acteth differently upon that which each particular passage thereof containeth; yielding obedience to the commands, trembling at the threatenings, and embracing the promises of God for this life, and that which is to come. But the principal acts of saving faith are accepting, receiving, and resting upon Christ alone for justification, sanctification, and eternal life, by virtue of the covenant of grace.
John 4:42; 1 Thess. 2:13; 1 John 5:10; Acts 24:14; Rom. 16:26;

3. Saving faith will normally come to expression in a public confession of Christ within the visible church.
Rom. 10:9.

4. *We reject* the doctrine of universal salvation.
Matt. 25:46; John 5:28-29; Rom. 2:6-13.

Isa. 66:2; Heb. 11:13; 1 Tim. 4:8; John 1:12; Acts 16:31; Gal. 2: 20; Acts 15:11.

5. *We reject* the idea that a man can be saved by any means other than faith in Jesus Christ.
1 Tim. 2:5; Rom. 3:28; John 14:6; Acts 4:12; Heb. 11:24-26.

6. *We reject* the idea that unregenerate people can be persuaded to believe without the ministry of the Holy Spirit.
Rom. 9:16; Titus 3:5.

7. *We reject* the concept that saving faith is merely agreeing that the Bible is historically accurate, and that the doctrines of the Bible are true.
Jas. 2:19.

8. The proper basis for believing is the infinite sufficiency of Christ to save, the unrestricted free invitation to come to Him for salvation, God's command to all to repent and believe, and the promise of salvation to those who believe and obey the Gospel.
Heb. 7:25; Isa. 55:1, 5, 7; Rev. 22:17; 1 John 3:23; Acts 16:31; Heb. 5:9.

3. This faith is different in degrees, weak or strong; may be often and many ways assailed, and weakened, but gets the victory; growing up in many to the attainment of a full assurance through Christ, who is both the author and finisher of our faith.
Heb. 5:13-14; Rom. 4:19-20; Matt. 6:30; Matt. 8:10; Luke 22: 31-32; Eph. 6:16; 1 John 5:4-5; Heb. 6:11-12; Heb. 10:22; Col. 2:2; Heb. 12:2.

9. God's offer of salvation is genuine, regardless of man's response.
John 6:35-37; Matt. 11:28-30; John 7:37; Rom. 3:4.

10. *We reject* the idea that saving faith is a man's persuading himself that he is elect, and that he has already been saved.
Prov. 14:12; 1 John 1:6-7; 1 John 2:4-5.

Chapter 15: Of Repentance Unto Life

(Larger Catechism: 76, 153, 194; Shorter Catechism: 85, 87)

1. Repentance unto life is an evangelical grace, the doctrine whereof is to be preached by every minister of the Gospel, as well as that of faith in Christ.
Zech. 12:10; Acts 11:18; Luke 24:47; Mark 1:5; Acts 20:21.

1. Repentance leads to eternal life only when it is accompanied by faith in Christ.
Acts 20:21; Mark 1:15.

2. By it, a sinner, out of the sight and sense not only of the danger, but also of the filthiness and odiousness of his sins, as contrary to the holy nature and righteous law of God; and upon the apprehension of His mercy in Christ to such as are penitent, so grieves for, and hates his sins, as to turn from them all unto God, purposing and endeavoring to walk with Him in all the ways of His commandments.

Ezek. 18:30-31; Ezek. 36:31; Isa. 30:22; Ps. 51:4; Jer. 31:18-19; Joel 2:12-13; Amos 5:15; Ps. 119:128; 2 Cor. 7:11; Ps. 119:6, 59, 106; Luke 1:6; 2 Kings 23:25.

3. Although repentance be not to be rested in, as any satisfaction for sin, or any cause of the pardon thereof, which is the act of God's free grace in Christ; yet is it of such necessity to all sinners, that none may expect pardon without it.
Ezek. 36:31-32; Ezek. 16:61-63; Hos. 14:2, 4; Rom. 3:24; Eph. 1:7; Luke 13:3, 5; Acts 17:30-31.

4. As there is no sin so small, but it deserves damnation, so there is no sin so great, that it can bring damnation upon those who truly repent.
Rom. 6:23; Rom. 5:12; Matt. 12:36; Isa. 55:7; Rom. 8:1; Isa. 1: 16, 18.

5. Men ought not to content themselves with a general repentance, but it is every man's duty to endeavour to repent of his particular sins, particularly.
Ps. 19:13; Luke 19:8; 1 Tim. 1:13, 15.

6. As every man is bound to make private confession of his sins to God, praying for the pardon thereof; upon which, and the forsaking of them, he shall find mercy; so, he that scandalizeth his brother, or the Church of Christ, ought to be willing, by a private or public confession, and sorrow for his sin, to declare his repentance to those that are offended, who are thereupon to be reconciled to him, and in love to receive him.
Ps. 51:4-5, 7, 9, 14; Ps. 32:5-6; Prov. 28:13; 1 John 1:9; Jas. 5:16; Luke 17:3-4; Josh. 7:19; Ps. 51; 2 Cor. 2:8.

2. Although a believer is freed from the penalty of sin by justification, he is still bound to give perfect obedience to God's law. Because of incomplete sanctification he is unable to do this, but daily breaks the commands of God in thought, word and deed. Therefore, all men are in continual need of repentance.
1 John 1:8-10; Rom. 7:14-25; 1 Tim. 1:15; Lev. 19:2; Eccl. 7:20; Gen. 8:21; John 13:10.

3. *We reject* the doctrine that Christians can in this life attain a condition in which they no longer have need of repentance.
1 Tim. 1:15.

4. Unregenerate men may, and often do, feel regret or remorse, realizing that sin brings shame and misery and is an obstacle to the happiness they seek; but they may not see sin as an offense against the holy God. Since they do not turn to God, they do not exercise true repentance.
2 Cor. 7:10; Heb. 12:16-17; Rom. 1:32.

5. The unpardonable sin is the rejection of the testimony of the Holy Spirit concerning Jesus Christ. It is the willful and persistent rejection of the only hope of forgiveness through the Savior.
Matt. 10:33; 2 Tim. 2:12.

6. Self-examination is essential to true repentance. A person must examine his life to detect specific sins, and repent of them.
Ps. 26; Ps. 139; Ps. 32:5-6; 1 John 1:9; Ps. 119:59; 2 Cor. 13:5.

7. Since sin is primarily an offense against God, confession to other men cannot take the place of repentance toward God. Since each one is to confess his sins to God, the source of forgiveness, he has no need of priest or other intermediary except Jesus Christ. He should also confess to men against whom he has sinned, and submit to all lawful penalties.
Ps. 32:5; Ps. 51:4; 1 Cor. 5:1-13; Jas. 5:16.

8. Every man bears a degree of responsibility for the sins of groups in which he participates. When sins are corporate, repentance and confession should be corporate as well as individual.
Josh. 7:11; Dan. 9:3-20; 2 Chron. 15:8-15; Neh. 9; Rev. 2:5, 16; Matt. 6:12.

9. Godly repentance implies true faith and union with Christ,

but is not the ground of pardon. It precedes the joy which flows from the assurance of pardon.
Zech. 12:10; Eph. 1:7; Rom. 3:28; Luke 13:3; Acts 3:19; Ps. 51:1, 8, 12; 2 Cor. 7:10.

Chapter 16: Of Good Works

(Larger Catechism: 60, 73, 78; Shorter Catechism: 35)

1. Good works are only such as God hath commanded in His holy Word, and not such as, without the warrant thereof, are devised by men, out of blind zeal, or upon any pretence of good intention.
Mic. 6:8; Rom. 12:2; Heb. 13:21; Matt. 15:9; Isa. 29:13; 1 Pet. 1:18; Rom. 10:2; John 16:2; 1 Sam. 15:21-23.

2. These good works, done in obedience to God's commandments, are the fruits and evidences of a true and lively faith: and by them believers manifest their thankfulness, strengthen their assurance, edify their brethren, adorn the profession of the Gospel, stop the mouths of the adversaries, and glorify God, whose workmanship they are, created in Christ Jesus thereunto; that, having their fruit unto holiness, they may have the end, eternal life.
Jas. 2:18, 22; Ps. 116:12-13; 1 Pet. 2:9; 1 John 2:3, 5; 2 Pet. 1:5-10; 2 Cor. 9:2; Matt. 5:16; Titus 2:5, 9-12; 1 Tim. 6:1; 1 Pet. 2:15; 1 Pet. 2:12; Phil. 1:11; John 15:8; Eph. 2:10; Rom. 6:22.

3. Their ability to do good works is not at all of themselves, but wholly from the Spirit of Christ. And that they may be enabled thereunto, besides the graces they have already received, there is required an actual influence of the same Holy Spirit, to work in them to will and to do of His good pleasure: yet are they not hereupon to grow negligent, as if they were not bound to perform any duty, unless upon a special motion of the Spirit; but they ought to be diligent in stirring up the grace of God that is in them.
John 15:4-5; Ezek. 36:26-27; Phil. 2:13; Phil. 4:13; 2 Cor. 3:5; Phil. 2:12; Heb. 6:11-12; 2 Pet. 1:3, 5, 10-11; Isa. 64:7; 2 Tim. 1:6; Acts 26:6-7; Jude 1:20-21.

4. They, who in their obedience attain to the greatest height which is possible in this life, are so far from being able to supererogate, and to do more than God requires, as that they fall short of much which in duty they are bound to do.
Luke 17:10; Neh. 13:22; Job 9:2-3; Gal. 5:17.

5. We cannot, by our best works, merit pardon of sin, or eternal life at the hand of God, by reason of the great disproportion

1. Good works, while not a means of salvation, are required of believers as a testimony to God's grace, as evidence of regeneration and as a blessing to mankind.
Matt. 5:16; Eph. 2:10; Titus 3:8-14.

2. *We reject* the notion that sincerity of performance, or the declaration of a church, can make any act a "good work."
Rom. 10:2; Matt. 15:9.

3. *We reject* the idea that we, by good works, can win favor with God, either for ourselves or for others.
Rom. 3:20; Isa. 64:6.

that is between them and the glory to come; and the infinite distance that is between us and God, whom, by them, we can neither profit, nor satisfy for the debt of our former sins, but when we have done all we can, we have done but our duty, and are unprofitable servants; and because, as they are good, they proceed from His Spirit; and as they are wrought by us, they are defiled, and mixed with so much weakness and imperfection, that they cannot endure the severity of God's judgment.
Rom. 3:20; Rom. 4:2, 4, 6; Eph. 2:8-9; Titus 3:5-7; Rom. 8:18; Ps. 16:2; Job 22:2-3; Job 35:7-8; Luke 17:10; Gal. 5:22-23; Isa. 64:6; Gal. 5:17; Rom. 7:15, 18; Ps. 143:2; Ps. 130:3.

6. Yet notwithstanding, the persons of believers being accepted through Christ, their good works also are accepted in Him, not as though they were in this life wholly unblameable and unreprovable in God's sight; but that He, looking upon them in His Son, is pleased to accept and reward that which is sincere, although accompanied with many weaknesses and imperfections.
Eph. 1:6; 1 Pet. 2:5; Ex. 28:38; Gen. 4:4 with Heb. 11:4; Job 9:20; Ps. 143:2; Heb. 13:20-21; 2 Cor. 8:12; Heb. 6:10; Matt. 25:21, 23.

7. Works done by unregenerate men, although, for the matter of them, they may be things which God commands, and of good use both to themselves and others: yet, because they proceed not from a heart purified by faith; nor are done in a right manner according to the Word; nor to a right end, the glory of God; they are therefore sinful, and cannot please God, or make a man meet to receive grace from God. And yet, their neglect of them is more sinful, and displeasing unto God.
2 Kings 10:30-31; 1 Kings 21:27, 29; Phil. 1:15-16, 18; Gen. 4:5 with Heb. 11:4, 6; 1 Cor. 13:3; Isa. 1:12; Matt. 6:2, 5, 16; Hag. 2:14; Titus 1:15; Amos 5:21-22; Hos. 1:4; Rom. 9:16; Titus 3:5; Ps. 14:4; Ps. 36:3; Job 21:14-15; Matt. 25:41-43, 45; Matt. 23:23.

4. By God's grace, many unregenerate men have generous impulses and may lead outwardly moral lives. Yet good works are only those things done in obedience to His revealed will, out of sincere love for Him and desire to serve Him. The Christian may work with unbelievers in seeking the good of society, but his chief motive should be the glory of God. Christians should avoid any voluntary association in which they cannot maintain a consistent testimony for Christ.
Rom. 14:23; Eph. 2:10; John 15:5; Rom. 12:1-2.

Chapter 17: Of the Perseverance of the Saints

(Larger Catechism: 79-81; Shorter Catechism: 35-36)

1. They, whom God hath accepted in His Beloved, effectually called, and sanctified by His Spirit, can neither totally, nor finally, fall away from the state of grace: but shall certainly persevere therein to the end, and be eternally saved.
Phil. 1:6; 2 Pet. 1:10; John 10:28-29; 1 John 3:9; 1 Pet. 1:5, 9.

1. Men may profess faith in Jesus Christ and have the outward appearance of being regenerate, for a time, and yet finally fall away from this profession.
Heb. 6:4-8; 2 Pet. 2:20-22.

2. *We reject* the view that, because it appears to happen in human observation, true believers can fall away and be eternally lost.
1 John 2:19.

3. The Church cannot discern hypocrites so long as they continue to profess the true religion, and appear obedient to the law of God.
1 Sam. 16:7.

4. *We reject* the view that the Church is able to judge the hearts of men.
Ps. 7:9; Ps. 75:7; Jer. 17:9-10.

2. This perseverance of the saints depends not upon their own free will, but upon the immutability of the decree of election, flowing from the free and unchangeable love of God the Father; upon the efficacy of the merit and intercession of Jesus Christ; the abiding of the Spirit, and of the seed of God within them; and the nature of the covenant of grace; from all which ariseth also the certainty and infallibility thereof.
2 Tim. 2:18-19; Jer. 31:3; Heb. 10:10, 14; Heb. 13:20-21; Heb. 9:12-15; Rom. 8:33-39; John 17:11, 24; Luke 22:32; Heb. 7:25; John 14:16-17; 1 John 2:27; 1 John 3:9; Jer. 32:40; John 10:28; 2 Thess. 3:3; 1 John 2:19.

3. Nevertheless, they may, through the temptations of Satan and of the world, the prevalency of corruption remaining in them, and the neglect of the means of their preservation, fall into grievous sins; and, for a time, continue therein: whereby they incur God's displeasure, and grieve His Holy Spirit, come to be deprived of some measure of their graces and comforts, have their hearts hardened, and their consciences wounded, hurt and scandalize others, and bring temporal judgments upon themselves.
Matt. 26:70, 72, 74; Ps. 51:title and vs. 14; Isa. 64:5, 7, 9; 2 Sam. 11:27; Eph. 4:30; Ps. 51:8, 10, 12; Rev. 2:4; Song of Sol. 5:2-4, 6; Isa. 63:17; Mark 6:52; Mark 16:14; Ps. 32:3-4; Ps. 51:8; 2 Sam. 12:14; Ps. 89:31-32; 1 Cor. 11:32.

5. *We reject* the accusation that the doctrine of the perseverance of the saints is opposed to the believers' responsibility to pursue their own growth in holiness.

Chapter 18: Of the Assurance of Grace and Salvation

(Larger Catechism: 80-81; Shorter Catechism: 36)

1. Although hypocrites and other unregenerate men may vainly deceive themselves with false hopes, and carnal presumptions of being in the favour of God, and estate of salvation; which hope of theirs shall perish: yet such as truly believe in the Lord Jesus, and love Him in sincerity, endeavouring to walk in all good conscience before Him, may, in this life, be certainly assured that they are in the state of grace, and may rejoice in the hope of the glory of God, which hope shall never make them ashamed.
Job 8:13-14; Mic. 3:11; Deut. 29:19; John 8:41; Matt. 7:22-23; 1 John 2:3; 1 John 3:14, 18-19, 21, 24; 1 John 5:13; Rom. 5:2, 5.

1. A man may believe himself to be saved when he is not. A man can also fear that he is not saved, when in actual fact he is.
Isa. 50:10; Luke 18:11-14.

2. The Holy Spirit gives assurance of salvation by leading believers to rest confidently on God's promises, producing in their lives the love for Christ and others which is the fruit of the new birth and enabling them to call upon God as their loving Father in heaven.
2 Tim. 1:12; John 14:21; 1 John 3:14; Rom. 8:14-16; 1 John 2:5; 1 John 5:13; John 10:27-28.

2. This certainty is not a bare conjectural and probable persuasion, grounded upon a fallible hope; but an infallible assurance of faith, founded upon the divine truth of the promises of salvation, the inward evidence of those graces unto which these promises are made, the testimony of the Spirit of adoption witnessing with our spirits that we are the children of God: which Spirit is the earnest of our inheritance, whereby we are sealed to the day of redemption.
Heb. 6:11, 19; Heb. 6:17-18; 2 Pet. 1:4-5, 10-11; 1 John 2:3; 1 John 3:14; 2 Cor. 1:12; Rom. 8:15-16; Eph. 1:13-14; Eph. 4:30; 2 Cor. 1:21-22.

3. Spiritual experiences or circumstances, however worthy, such as birth of Christian parents, church membership, participation in the sacraments, the hearing of the Word, good works, response to an altar call, speaking in tongues, and other real or imagined evidences of grace, do not of themselves constitute a basis for assurance of salvation.
Rom. 9:7; Rom. 2:28-29; 1 Cor. 10:1-12; Heb. 4:2; Acts 8:9-24; 1 Cor. 11:27-29; Heb. 10:38-39; Titus 3:5.

4. *We reject* the view that, without saving faith, participation in the sacraments or the use of any other means of grace is a proper basis of assurance.

5. *We reject* the teaching that assurance must be chiefly based upon one's memory of a particular conversion experience.

3. This infallible assurance doth not so belong to the essence of faith, but that a true believer may wait long, and conflict with many difficulties before he be partaker of it: yet, being enabled by the Spirit to know the things which are freely given him of God, he may without extraordinary revelation, in the right use of ordinary means, attain thereunto. And therefore it is the duty of everyone to give all diligence to make his calling and election sure; that thereby his heart may be enlarged in peace and joy in the Holy Ghost, in love and thankfulness to God, and in strength and cheerfulness in the duties of obedience, the proper fruits of this assurance; so far is it from inclining men to looseness.
1 John 5:13; Isa. 50:10; Mark 9:24; Ps. 88; Ps. 77:1-12; 1 Cor. 2:12; 1 John 4:13; Heb. 6:11-12; Eph. 3:17-19; 2 Pet. 1:10; Rom. 5:1-2, 5; Rom. 14:17; Rom. 15:13; Eph. 1:3-4; Ps. 4:6-7; Ps. 119:32; 1 John 2:1-2; Rom. 6:1-2; Titus 2:11-12, 14; 2 Cor. 7:1; Rom. 8:1, 12; 1 John 3:2-3; Ps. 130:4; 1 John 1:6-7.

6. It is the task of the Church to declare the Word of God so that the believer, being enabled by the Holy Spirit, can discern his own true inward condition, and thus know that he is saved; but it is not the proper function of the minister or any other person to tell people whether they are saved.
Rom. 8:16.

7. *We reject* the view that preaching the Gospel consists merely in urging people to assent to its truth.

8. While the Scriptures require self-examination, a believer must remember that his heart can be deceived, and that he is always subject to the temptation to trust in works rather than in Christ. A person should not lightly assume he is saved.
1 Cor. 11:28, 32; Prov. 28:26; 1 John 3:19-24; Gal. 6:3; Rev. 3:17-18.

4. True believers may have the assurance of their salvation divers ways shaken, diminished, and intermitted; as, by negligence in preserving of it, by falling into some special sin, which woundeth the conscience and grieveth the Spirit; by some sudden or vehement temptation, by God's withdrawing the light of His countenance, and suffering even such as fear Him to walk in darkness and to have no light: yet are they never utterly destitute of that seed of God, and life of faith, that love of Christ and the brethren, that sincerity of heart, and conscience of duty, out of which, by the operation of the Spirit, this assurance may, in due time, be revived; and by the which, in the mean time, they are supported from utter despair.
Song of Sol. 5:2-3, 6; Ps. 51:8, 12, 14; Eph. 4:30-31; Ps. 77:1-10; Matt. 26:69-72; Ps. 31:22; Ps. 88; Isa. 50:10; 1 John 3:9; Luke 22:32; Job 13:15; Ps. 73:15; Ps. 51:8, 12; Isa. 50:10; Mic. 7:7-9; Jer. 32:40; Isa. 54:7-10; Ps. 22:1; Ps. 88.

9. A believer's lack of assurance may evidence sinful neglect. Fear respecting the state of a man's own heart is not necessarily the sin of unbelief, for unbelief consists in rejecting the Gospel, not in questioning the presence of grace in the heart.
2 Cor. 13:5.

10. *We reject* the teaching that a full assurance of salvation is so inseparably connected with saving faith that a believer cannot be saved without it.

11. *We reject* the teaching that assurance of salvation leads to complacency, or is unimportant to the life and walk of faith, to prayer, and to good works.

Chapter 19: Of the Law of God

(Larger Catechism: 91-148; Shorter Catechism: 40-81)

1. God gave to Adam a law, as a covenant of works, by which He bound him and all his posterity to personal, entire, exact, and perpetual obedience; promised life upon the fulfilling, and threatened death upon the breach of it: and endued him with power and ability to keep it.
Gen. 1:26-27 with Gen. 2:17; Rom. 2:14-15; Rom. 10:5; Rom. 5:12, 19; Gal. 3:10, 12; Eccl. 7:29; Job 28:28.

2. This law, after his fall, continued to be a perfect rule of righteousness, and, as such, was delivered by God upon Mount Sinai, in ten commandments, and written in two tables: the four first commandments containing our duty towards God; and the other six our duty to man.
Jas. 1:25; Jas. 2:8, 10-12; Rom. 13:8-9; Deut. 5:32; Deut. 10:4; Ex. 34:1; Matt. 22:37-40.

1. This law is still the rule of God's judgment of men. Christ has fulfilled the requirements of the law for His people by His perfect obedience and His propitiation for their sins.
Gal. 3:10-14; Matt. 5:17-18.

3. Beside this law, commonly called moral, God was pleased to give to the people of Israel, as a church under age, ceremonial laws, containing several typical ordinances, partly of worship, prefiguring Christ, His graces, actions, sufferings, and benefits; and partly holding forth divers instructions of moral duties. All which ceremonial laws are now abrogated, under the New Testament.
Heb. 9; Heb. 10:1; Gal. 4:1-3; Col. 2:17; 1 Cor. 5:7; 2 Cor. 6:17; Jude 1:23; Col. 2:14, 16-17; Dan. 9:27; Eph. 2:15-16.

2. The ceremonial laws were fulfilled by Christ as our high priest and are no longer binding.
Heb. 10:1-22.

4. To them also, as a body politic, He gave sundry judicial laws, which expired together with the State of that people; not obliging any other now, further than the general equity thereof may require.
Ex. 21; Ex. 22:1-29; Gen. 49:10 with 1 Pet. 2:13-14; Matt. 5:17, 38-39; 1 Cor. 9:8-10.

5. The moral law doth for ever bind all, as well justified persons as others, to the obedience thereof; and that, not only in regard of the matter contained in it, but also in respect of the authority of God the Creator, who gave it: neither doth Christ, in the Gospel, any way dissolve, but much strengthen this obligation.
Rom. 13:8-10; Eph. 6:2; 1 John 2:3-4, 7-8; Jas. 2:10-11; Matt. 5:17-19; Jas. 2:8; Rom. 3:31.

3. *We reject* the teaching that believers are not required to keep all of the Ten Commandments under the New Testament.
Matt. 5:19-20.

6. Although true believers be not under the law, as a covenant of works, to be thereby justified or condemned; yet is it of great use to them, as well as to others; in that, as a rule of life informing them of the will of God, and their duty, it directs, and binds them to walk accordingly; discovering also the sinful pollutions of their nature, hearts, and lives; so as, examining

themselves thereby, they may come to further conviction of, humiliation for, and hatred against sin; together with a clearer sight of the need they have of Christ, and the perfection of His obedience. It is likewise of use to the regenerate, to restrain their corruptions, in that it forbids sin; and the threatenings of it serve to show what even their sins deserve; and what afflictions, in this life, they may expect for them, although freed from the curse thereof threatened in the law. The promises of it, in like manner, show them God's approbation of obedience, and what blessings they may expect upon the performance thereof; although not as due to them by the law, as a covenant of works. So as, a man's doing good, and refraining from evil, because the law encourageth to the one, and deterreth from the other, is no evidence of his being under the law; and not under grace.
Rom. 6:14; Gal. 2:16; Gal. 3:13; Gal. 4:4-5; Acts 13:39; Rom. 8:1; Rom. 7:12, 22, 25; Ps. 119:4-6; 1 Cor. 7:19; Gal. 5:14, 16, 18-23; Rom. 7:7; Rom. 3:20; Jas. 1:23-25; Rom. 7:9, 14, 24; Gal. 3:24; Rom. 7:24-25; Rom. 8:3-4; Jas. 2:11; Ps. 119:101, 104, 128; Ezra 9:13-14; Ps. 89:30-34; Lev. 26:1-14 with 2 Cor. 6:16; Eph. 6:2-3; Ps. 37:11 with Matt. 5:5; Ps. 19:11; Gal. 2:16; Luke 17:10; Rom. 6:12, 14; 1 Pet. 3:8-12 with Ps. 34:12-16; Heb. 12:28-29.

4. A believer's obedience to the law of God is a proper expression of his thankfulness for the love which he has experienced in the Savior.
John 14:15.

5. *We reject* the view that obedience to God's law is sinful legalism.

6. Sinful legalism consists of mere outward conformity to the law in the absence of love to the Lawgiver. It often involves the effort to gain salvation or reward through such obedience, and the tendency to require of others a similar pattern of conduct. It may also involve adding human requirements that evade God's law.
Matt. 23:13-31; Mark 7:1-23.

7. Neither are the forementioned uses of the law contrary to the grace of the Gospel, but do sweetly comply with it; the Spirit of Christ subduing and enabling the will of man to do that, freely and cheerfully, which the will of God, revealed in the law, requireth to be done.
Gal. 3:21; Ezek. 36:27; Heb. 8:10 with Jer. 31:33.

Chapter 20: Of Christian Liberty, and Liberty of Conscience

(Larger Catechism: 28, 45, 83; Shorter Catechism: 2, 26)

1. The liberty which Christ hath purchased for believers under the Gospel consists in their freedom from the guilt of sin, the condemning wrath of God, the curse of the moral law; and, in their being delivered from this present evil world, bondage to Satan, and dominion of sin; from the evil of afflictions, the sting of death, the victory of the grave, and everlasting damnation; as also, in their free access to God, and their yielding obedience unto Him, not out of slavish fear, but a child-like love and willing mind. All which were common also to believers under the law. But, under the new testament, the liberty of Christians is further enlarged, in their freedom from the yoke of the ceremonial law, to which the Jewish Church was subjected; and in greater boldness of access to the throne of grace, and in fuller communications of the free Spirit of God, than believers under the law did ordinarily partake of.
Titus 2:14; 1 Thess. 1:10; Gal. 3:13; Gal. 1:4; Col. 1:13; Acts 26:

1. Christian liberty consists primarily in the believer's freedom from the guilt and power of sin, in freedom from the ceremonial law and in freedom of access to God through Christ.
Titus 2:14; Rom. 6:17-19, 22; Gal. 5:1; Acts 15:10-11; Heb. 10:19-22.

2. Christ sets believers free not only from a feeling of guilt, but from actual guilt.

3. *We reject* the teaching that believers under the Old Testament had no such liberty as belongs to believers under the New Testament. The difference between the liberty enjoyed under the Old and New Testaments is one of degree rather than kind.
Ps. 32:1-5; Ps. 130:7-8.

18; Rom. 6:14; Rom. 8:28; Ps. 119:71; 1 Cor. 15:54-57; Rom. 8:1; Rom. 5:1-2; Rom. 8:14-15; 1 John 4:18; Gal. 3:9, 14; Gal. 4:1-3, 6-7; Gal. 5:1; Acts 15:10-11; Heb. 4:14, 16; Heb. 10:19-22; John 7:38-39; 2 Cor. 3:13, 17-18.

2. God alone is Lord of the conscience, and hath left it free from the doctrines and commandments of men, which are in any thing contrary to His Word; or beside it, if matters of faith or worship. So that, to believe such doctrines, or to obey such commands, out of conscience, is to betray true liberty of conscience: and the requiring of an implicit faith, and an absolute and blind obedience is to destroy liberty of conscience, and reason also.
Jas. 4:12; Rom. 14:4; Acts 4:19; Acts 5:29; 1 Cor. 7:23; Matt. 23:8-10; 2 Cor. 1:24; Matt. 15:9; Col. 2:20, 22-23; Gal. 1:10; Gal. 2:4-5; Gal. 5:1; Rom. 10:17; Rom. 14:23; Isa. 8:20; Acts 17:11; John 4:22; Hos. 5:11; Rev. 13:12, 16-17; Jer. 8:9.

3. They who, upon pretence of Christian liberty, do practice any sin, or cherish any lust, do thereby destroy the end of Christian liberty, which is, that being delivered out of the hands of our enemies, we might serve the Lord without fear, in holiness and righteousness before Him, all the days of our life.
Gal. 5:13; 1 Pet. 2:16; 2 Pet. 2:19; John 8:34; Luke 1:74-75.

4. And because the powers which God hath ordained, and the liberty which Christ hath purchased, are not intended by God to destroy, but mutually to uphold and preserve one another; they who, upon pretence of Christian liberty, shall oppose any lawful power, or the lawful exercise of it, whether it be civil or ecclesiastical, resist the ordinance of God. And, for their publishing of such opinions, or maintaining of such practices, as are contrary to the light of nature, or to the known principles of Christianity, whether concerning faith, worship or conversation; or, to the power of godliness; or, such erroneous opinions or practices, as either in their own nature, or in the manner of publishing or maintaining them, are destructive to the external peace and order which Christ hath established in the Church, they may lawfully be called to account, and proceeded against by the censures of the Church, and by the power of the civil magistrate.
Matt. 12:25; 1 Pet. 2:13-14, 16; Rom. 13:1-8; Heb. 13:17; Rom. 1:32 with 1 Cor. 5:1, 5, 11, 13; 2 John 10-11, and 2 Thess. 3:14, and 1 Tim. 6:3-5, and Titus 1:10-11, 13, and Titus 3:10 with Matt. 18:15-17; 1 Tim. 1:19-20; Rev. 2:2, 14-15, 20; Rev. 3:9; Deut. 13:6-12; Rom. 13:3-4 with 2 John 10-11; Ezra 7:23, 25-28; Rev. 17:12, 16-17; Neh. 13:15, 17, 21-22, 25, 30; 2 Kings 23:5-6, 9, 20-21; 2 Chron. 34:33; 2 Chron. 15:12-13, 16; Dan. 3:29; 1 Tim. 2:2; Isa. 49:23; Zech. 13:2-3.

4. Conscience is a sense of right and wrong by which one evaluates his own thoughts and behavior. When one follows his conscience, he feels a measure of contentment; when he violates his conscience, he feels distress. Conscience is natural to man, and implies his accountability to God, but it is not the rule of faith and practice. Conscience shows the work of the law written on the heart, but is distorted by the work of Satan, by man's sinful nature, and by the ungodly standards of the world. The Christian's conscience is to be directed by God's revealed law, under the illumination of the Holy Spirit, with due attention to the teaching and admonition of the brethren. Although conscience is not infallible, a person should not do what he believes to be wrong.
Rom. 2:14-15; 2 Cor. 4:4; 1 Tim. 4:2-3; Rom. 12:1-2; Matt. 15:9; 2 Tim. 3:16-17; Ps. 143:10; Rom. 8:5-9; Col. 3:16; Rom. 14:14, 23.

5. Liberty of conscience differs from Christian liberty. Liberty of conscience is the freedom to interpret and apply God's Word to one's own life. The Christian is to render due submission in the Lord to any lawful authority, but he has the right to disagree with any improper use of human authority. If that authority requires him to sin, he must obey God rather than man. Individual liberty is regulated by the principles found in Scripture and is limited by the mutual duties believers owe to one another, and by concern for the welfare of all men.
Rom. 13:1-7; Acts 5:29; 1 Pet. 2:13-16; 1 Cor. 10:27-29; Rom. 14:10-15; 1 Cor. 8:9-15; Titus 3:1; Gal. 5:13-18.

6. The civil magistrate has no authority to pronounce ecclesiastical censures.

Chapter 21: Of Religious Worship, and the Sabbath Day

(Larger Catechism: 103-121, 178-196; Shorter Catechism: 45-62, 88-90, 98-107)

1. The light of nature showeth that there is a God, who hath lordship and sovereignty over all, is good, and doth good unto all, and is therefore to be feared, loved, praised, called upon, trusted in, and served, with all the heart, and with all the soul, and with all the might. But the acceptable way of worshipping the true God is instituted by Himself, and so limited by His own revealed will, that He may not be worshipped according to the imaginations and devices of men, or the suggestions of Satan, under any visible representation, or any other way not prescribed in the holy Scripture.
Rom. 1:20; Acts 17:24; Ps. 119:68; Jer. 10:7; Ps. 31:23; Ps. 18:3; Rom. 10:12; Ps. 62:8; Josh. 24:14; Mark 12:33; Deut. 12:32; Matt. 15:9; Acts 17:25; Matt. 4:9-10; Deut. 4:15-20; Ex. 20:4-6; Col. 2:23.

1. All people are required to worship the true God, in a scriptural manner, with sincerity of heart. Sincerity cannot make unscriptural worship acceptable to God. Proper worship is to be conducted in an orderly manner. The tendency to emphasize ritual, liturgy and ceremony is contrary to the Scriptures.
Acts 24:16; John 16:2; Isa. 1:11-15; John 4:24; Heb. 10:19-22.

2. Worship is to be offered only in accordance with God's appointment, and in harmony with the scriptural principle that whatever is not commanded in the worship of God, by precept or example, is forbidden.
Lev. 10:1-3; 2 Sam. 6:1-11; Matt. 15:8-9.

3. The use of pictures or images of Jesus in worship, or as aids to devotion, is unscriptural. The Scriptures do not provide a sufficient description of His physical appearance to picture Him. The work of artists should not be received as accurate representations of His Person.
Ex. 20:4-5.

2. Religious worship is to be given to God, the Father, Son, and Holy Ghost; and to Him alone; not to angels, saints, or any other creature: and since the fall, not without a Mediator; nor in the mediation of any other but of Christ alone.
Matt. 4:10 with John 5:23 and 2 Cor. 13:14; Col. 2:18; Rev. 19:10; Rom. 1:25; John 14:6; 1 Tim. 2:5; Eph. 2:18; Col. 3:17.

3. Prayer, with thanksgiving, being one special part of religious worship, is by God required of all men: and that it may be accepted, it is to be made in the name of the Son, by the help of His Spirit, according to His will, with understanding, reverence, humility, fervency, faith, love, and perseverance; and, if vocal, in a known tongue.
Phil. 4:6; Ps. 65:2; John 14:13-14; 1 Pet. 2:5; Rom. 8:26; 1 John 5:14; Ps. 47:7; Eccl. 5:1-2; Heb. 12:28; Gen. 18:27; Jas. 5:16; Jas. 1:6-7; Mark 11:24; Matt. 6:12, 14-15; Col. 4:2; Eph. 6:18; 1 Cor. 14:14.

4. Prayer is to be made for things lawful, and for all sorts of men living, or that shall live hereafter: but not for the dead, nor for those of whom it may be known that they have sinned the sin unto death.
1 John 5:14; 1 Tim. 2:1-2; John 17:20; 2 Sam. 7:29; Ruth 4:12; 2 Sam. 12:21-23 with Luke 16:25-26; Rev. 14:13; 1 John 5:16.

5. The reading of the Scriptures with godly fear; the sound preaching and conscionable hearing of the Word, in obedience unto God, with understanding, faith, reverence; singing of psalms with grace in the heart; as also, the due administration and worthy receiving of the sacraments instituted by Christ; are all parts of the ordinary religious worship of God: beside religious oaths, vows, solemn fastings, and thanksgivings, upon special occasions, which are, in their several times and seasons, to be used in a holy and religious manner.
Acts 15:21; Rev. 1:3; 2 Tim. 4:2; Jas. 1:22; Acts 10:33; Matt. 13: 19; Heb. 4:2; Isa. 66:2; Col. 3:16; Eph. 5:19; Jas. 5:13; Matt. 28: 19; 1 Cor. 11:23-29; Acts 2:42; Deut. 6:13 with Neh. 10:29; Isa. 19:21 with Eccl. 5:4-5; Joel 2:12; Esther 4:16; Matt. 9:15; 1 Cor. 7:5; Ps. 107; Esther 9:22; Heb. 12:28.

4. Public prayer is to accompany the reading and preaching of the Word.
Acts 2:42; 1 Cor. 14:13-19.

5. Singing God's praise is part of public worship in which the whole congregation should join. The Book of Psalms, consisting of inspired psalms, hymns and songs, is the divinely authorized manual of praise. The use of other songs in worship is not authorized in the Scriptures. The Greek words in the New Testament which are translated "psalm," "hymn" and "song" all appear in the Septuagint (Greek) version of the Book of Psalms.
Ps. 95:2; Ps. 40:3, (4); Ps. 96:1; Col. 3:16; Eph. 5:19; Mark 14: 26; 1 Cor 14:26; Jas. 5:13.

6. The Psalms are to be sung without the accompaniment of instruments, which are not part of the New Testament pattern of worship. Musical instruments were commanded for use with the offering of sacrifices in the Old Testament temple worship. The death of Christ being the perfect and final sacrifice brought an end to this way of worship. There is neither command for nor example of the use of musical instruments in the words or practice of Christ and the apostles. The command of the New Testament is to offer the sacrifice of praise—the fruit of our lips.
Num. 10:10; 2 Chron. 29:25-30; Heb. 9:12; Heb. 13:15.

7. Religious fasting is an ordinance of God in which the believer voluntarily abstains from food for a season for the purpose of seeking the will of God, strength for service or deeper spirituality. It should be accompanied by meditation, self-examination, humiliation before God, confession of sin, repentance and renewed dedication to a life of obedience.
Ex. 34:28; 1 Kings 19:8; Dan. 10:2-3; Joel 1:14; Joel 2:12-13, 15; Matt. 4:2; Matt. 6:16-18; Mark 9:29; Acts 13:2-3.

8. The presentation of tithes and offerings is warranted as part of worship.
1 Cor. 16:1-2; Mal. 3:10; 1 Chron. 29:6-13; Ex. 23:15.

6. Neither prayer, nor any other part of religious worship, is now under the Gospel either tied unto, or made more acceptable by any place in which it is performed, or towards which it is directed: but God is to be worshipped everywhere, in spirit and truth; as in private families daily, and in secret each one by himself; so, more solemnly, in the public assemblies, which are not carelessly or wilfully to be neglected, or forsaken, when God, by His Word or providence, calleth thereunto.
John 4:21; Mal. 1:11; 1 Tim. 2:8; John 4:23-24; Jer. 10:25; Deut. 6:6-7; Job 1:5; 2 Sam. 6:18, 20; 1 Pet. 3:7; Acts 10:2; Matt. 6:11; Matt. 6:6; Eph. 6:18; Isa. 56:6-7; Heb. 10:25; Prov. 1:20-21, 24; Prov. 8:34; Acts 13:42; Luke 4:16; Acts 2:42.

9. Heads of families are responsible for leadership in family worship.
Gen. 18:19; Eph. 6:4.

10. Worship in small groups is also encouraged by the Scripture.
Acts 5:42; Acts 12:12.

7. As it is the law of nature, that, in general, a due proportion of time be set apart for the worship of God; so, in His Word, by a positive, moral, and perpetual commandment, binding all men, in all ages, He hath particularly appointed one day in seven, for a Sabbath, to be kept holy unto Him: which, from the beginning of the world to the resurrection of Christ, was the last day of the week; and, from the resurrection of Christ, was changed into the first day of the week, which, in Scripture, is called the Lord's Day, and is to be continued to the end of the world, as the Christian Sabbath.
Ex. 20:8, 10-11; Isa. 56:2, 4, 6-7; Gen. 2:2-3; 1 Cor. 16:1-2; Acts 20:7; Rev. 1:10; Ex. 20:8, 10 with Matt. 5:17-18.

11. *We reject* the teaching that the Fourth Commandment is no longer binding under the New Testament.

8. This Sabbath is then kept holy unto the Lord, when men, after a due preparing of their hearts, and ordering of their common affairs beforehand, do not only observe an holy rest, all the day, from their own works, words, and thoughts about their worldly employments, and recreations, but also are taken up the whole time in the public and private exercises of His worship, and in the duties of necessity and mercy.
Ex. 20:8; Ex. 16:23, 25-26, 29-30; Ex. 31:15-17; Isa. 58:13; Neh. 13:15-19, 21-22; Isa. 58:13; Matt. 12:1-13.

12. God promises rich blessings for keeping the Lord's Day holy.
Isa. 56:2-7; Isa. 58:13-14; Mark 2:27.

Chapter 22: Of Lawful Oaths and Vows

(Larger Catechism: 108, 113; Shorter Catechism: 50, 55)

1. A lawful oath is a part of religious worship, wherein, upon just occasion, the person swearing solemnly calleth God to witness what he asserteth, or promiseth; and to judge him according to the truth or falsehood of what he sweareth.
Deut. 10:20; Ex. 20:7; Lev. 19:12; 2 Cor. 1:23; 2 Chron. 6:22-23.

1. There is scriptural warrant for swearing with the hand uplifted. Christians should avoid all superstitious or pagan customs in taking an oath.
Heb. 6:16-18; Gen. 14:22; Deut. 10:20; Ex. 6:8; Rev. 10:5-6.

2. The name of God only is that by which men ought to swear; and therein it is to be used with all holy fear and reverence. Therefore, to swear vainly or rashly, by that glorious and dreadful Name; or, to swear at all by any other thing, is sinful, and to be abhorred. Yet, as in matters of weight and moment, an oath is warranted by the Word of God, under the New Testament, as well as under the Old; so a lawful oath, being imposed by lawful authority, in such matters ought to be taken.
Deut. 6:13; Ex. 20:7; Jer. 5:7; Matt. 5:34, 37; Jas. 5:12; Heb. 6:16; 2 Cor. 1:23; Isa. 65:16; 1 Kings 8:31; Neh. 13:25; Ezra 10:5.

2. Those Scripture passages warning against taking oaths are to be understood as forbidding profane swearing, or the use of an oath to deceive or to escape one's duty.
Matt. 5:33-37; Jas. 5:12; cf. Mark 7:6-13.

3. The administrator of an oath, whether civil or ecclesiastical, ought to explain the meaning of the oath, and administer it with suitable solemnity. The well-being of individuals and of society requires that the administrator of an oath know and fear God and understand its nature. Oaths should be administered only to those who understand their meaning.
Eccl. 9:2; Deut. 6:13; Josh. 9:15, 19; cf. 2 Sam. 21:1-14.

3. Whosoever taketh an oath ought duly to consider the weightiness of so solemn an act; and therein to avouch nothing, but what he is fully persuaded is the truth. Neither may any man bind himself by oath to anything but what is

good and just, and what he believeth so to be, and what he is able and resolved to perform. Yet is it a sin to refuse an oath touching anything that is good and just, being imposed by lawful authority.

Ex. 20:7; Jer. 4:2; Gen. 24:2-3, 5-6, 8-9; Num. 5:19, 21; Neh. 5:12; Ex. 22:7-11.

4. An oath is to be taken in the plain and common sense of the words, without equivocation, or mental reservation. It cannot oblige to sin: but in anything not sinful, being taken, it binds to performance, although to a man's own hurt. Nor is it to be violated, although made to heretics, or infidels.

Jer. 4:2; Ps. 24:4; 1 Sam. 25:22, 32-34; Ps. 15:4; Ezek. 17:16, 18-19; Josh. 9:18-19 with 2 Sam. 21:1.

5. A vow is of the like nature with a promissory oath, and ought to be made with the like religious care, and to be performed with the like faithfulness.

Isa. 19:21; Eccl. 5:4-6; Ps. 61:8; Ps. 66:13-14.

6. It is not to be made to any creature, but to God alone: and, that it may be accepted, it is to be made voluntarily, out of faith, and conscience of duty, in way of thankfulness for mercy received, or for the obtaining of what we want; whereby we more strictly bind ourselves to necessary duties; or to other things, so far and so long as they may fitly conduce thereunto.

Ps. 76:11; Jer. 44:25-26; Deut. 23:21-23; Ps. 50:14; Gen. 28:20-22; 1 Sam. 1:11; Ps. 66:13-14; Ps. 132:2-5.

7. No man may vow to do anything forbidden in the Word of God, or what would hinder any duty therein commanded, or which is not in his own power, and for the performance whereof he hath no promise of ability from God. In which respects, Popish monastical vows of perpetual single life, professed poverty, and regular obedience, are so far from being degrees of higher perfection, that they are superstitious and sinful snares, in which no Christian may entangle himself.

Acts 23:12, 14; Mark 6:26; Num. 30:5, 8, 12-13; Matt. 19:11-12; 1 Cor. 7:2, 9; Eph. 4:28; 1 Pet. 4:2; 1 Cor. 7:23.

4. An oath is a confirmatory act calling God to witness the performance of a promise. An oath may confirm a vow or a covenant.

Num. 30:1-4; Ps. 132:2-5; Josh. 9:16-27; 2 Chron. 15:12-15.

5. A vow in Scripture is an act of voluntary dedication to God of one's person, goods or service. A vow is usually made by an individual.

Lev. 27; Num. 6; Deut. 23:21-23; cf. Num. 21:2; Nah. 1:15.

6. While it is sometimes difficult to distinguish between the uses in Scripture of the words "vow" and "covenant," a covenant that men make with God differs from a vow in that it is a corporate act of pledging obedience to what God has commanded in His covenant.

Gen. 28:20-22; Num. 21:2; Deut. 23:21-23; Josh. 24:24-25; 2 Chron. 34:29-32.

7. God has established two covenants with men: the Covenant of Works and the Covenant of Grace (see chap. 7). In accomplishing the Covenant of Grace God made covenants with Noah, Abraham, Israel at Sinai (renewed in the plain of Moab), and with David; these were fulfilled in the new covenant by Jesus Christ.

Gen. 2:17; Gen. 9:1-17; Gen. 12:1-3; Ex. 24:3-11; Deut. 29—30; 2 Sam. 7:5-16; Jer. 31:31-34.

8. God's covenants require obedience of all men whether they acknowledge their obligation or not. God's people, individually and corporately, respond to His covenants by solemnly promising to be the Lord's and to keep His commandments. The Old Testament sacraments, such as circumcision, passover and the feast of tabernacles, were means of entering into and periodically renewing Israel's covenant. Likewise, the sacraments of the New Testament are ordinances for entrance into and renewal of covenant union with God. In addition to these prescribed times of covenant celebration, God's people under the old covenant engaged in corporate acts of repentance and renewal in relation to the transgression of specific commandments or to general apostasy from God. Scripture calls such acts "covenants."
Gen. 17:10; Lev. 23:3-10 with John 19:36 and 1 Cor. 5:7-8; Matt. 26:26-29; 1 Cor. 11:23-26; Josh. 24:24-25; 2 Chron. 15:2, 8-15; 2 Chron. 23:16; 2 Chron. 34:29-32; Neh. 9-10.

9. Covenanting in the New Testament takes the form of confessing Christ and His Lordship. In view of the continued emphasis of the covenantal relationship of God to men in the New Testament, it is appropriate for churches and nations to covenant to be the Lord's and to serve Him. The statements or documents produced in these acts of covenant response are dependent upon the Covenant of Grace. They are statements of responsibility arising from the application of the Word of God to the times in which they are made. Such covenants have continuing validity in so far as they give true expression to the Word of God for the times and situations in which believers live.
Isa. 45:23 with Rom. 14:11 and Phil. 2:11; Jer. 31:31 with Heb. 8:6-13; Ex. 19:5-6 with 1 Pet. 2:9-10.

Chapter 23: Of the Civil Magistrate

(Larger Catechism: 135, 136)

1. God, the supreme Lord and King of all the world, hath ordained civil magistrates, to be, under Him, over the people, for His own glory, and the public good; and, to this end, hath armed them with the power of the sword, for the defence and encouragement of them that are good, and for the punishment of evildoers.
Rom. 13:1-4; 1 Pet. 2:13-14.

1. *We reject* the belief that civil government is unnecessary or essentially evil.

2. God has given the exercise of all authority to the Lord Jesus Christ. Christ is the Divine Lawgiver, Governor and Judge. His will concerning the purpose of civil government and the principles regarding its functions and operation are revealed in the written Word of God. The Holy Spirit enables even unregenerate rulers to fulfill their proper functions. A true

recognition of the authority and law of Christ in national life can only be the fruit of the Spirit's regenerating power in the lives of individuals.

Deut. 4:39; Dan. 4:25, 32, 35; Matt. 28:18; Phil. 2:10; Eph. 1:22; Isa. 33:22; Deut. 17:18-19; Isa. 45:1-7; Ezek. 36:27.

3. God has assigned to people, both individually and collectively, the responsibility for establishing and maintaining civil government, and the people are accountable to Jesus Christ for the proper exercise of this responsibility.

Deut. 1:13-14; Deut. 17:15; 1 Sam. 8:22; 2 Sam. 5:3; Hos. 8:1, 4; Eccl. 10:16-17.

4. Every nation ought to recognize the Divine institution of civil government, the sovereignty of God exercised by Jesus Christ, and its duty to rule the civil affairs of men in accordance with the will of God. It should enter into covenant with Christ and serve to advance His Kingdom on earth. The negligence of civil government in any of these particulars is sinful, makes the nation liable to the wrath of God, and threatens the continued existence of the government and nation.

Phil. 2:10; Rom. 13:4; Ps. 132:12; Ps. 103:17-19; Ps. 2:10-12.

5. *We reject* the view that nations have no corporate responsibility for acknowledging and obeying Christ.

6. It is the duty of every Christian citizen to labor and pray for his nation's official and explicit recognition of the authority and law of Jesus Christ, Preserver and Ruler of nations, and for the conduct of all governmental affairs in harmony with the written Word of God.

1 Tim. 2:1-2; Phil. 2:9-10; Acts 2:1-39; Ps. 2:8-12; Esther 4:14.

7. *We deny* that constitutional recognition of Jesus Christ means union of church and state.

8. *We reject* the teaching that Christians should not seek the establishment of Christian civil government.

9. No particular form of civil government is commanded in the Scriptures. Any form of civil government which observes the duties and limitations set upon it by God in His revealed Word is acceptable to God.

Ex. 18:21-24; Prov. 29:14; Deut. 1:16-17.

10. *We deny* that simply having a democratic or republican form of government insures God's approval and blessing.

11. All officers and employees of a civil government are to be servants of God for good. They are responsible to God for the discharge of lawful duties rightfully assigned to them by

human authority. Neither their official position, however, nor the orders of their superiors, nor the will of the people, exonerates them from blame for any unscriptural action or inaction.
Rom. 13:3-4; 2 Chron. 19:6-7; Prov. 29:26.

2. It is lawful for Christians to accept and execute the office of a magistrate, when called thereunto; in the managing whereof, as they ought especially to maintain piety, justice, and peace, according to the wholesome laws of each commonwealth; so for that end, they may lawfully now, under the New Testament, wage war, upon just and necessary occasion.
Prov. 8:15-16; Rom. 13:1-2, 4; Ps. 2:10-12; 1 Tim. 2:2; Ps. 82:3-4; 2 Sam. 23:3; 1 Pet. 2:13; Luke 3:14; Rom. 13:4; Matt. 8:9-10; Acts 10:1-2; Rev. 17:14, 16.

12. *We reject* the view that it is wrong to wage war in defense of life, liberty or religion.

13. Citizens cannot abdicate their responsibility to determine the moral legitimacy of a particular war and to govern their participation accordingly. Such decisions should be made prayerfully in the light of Scripture and with the counsel of the church.
Acts 5:29; 1 Sam. 14:44-45.

14. When justly administered, capital punishment is a scriptural application of civil authority.
Rom. 13:4; Gen. 9:6; Acts 25:11; Num. 35:29-34.

15. The Christian, when such action involves no disloyalty to Christ, ought to be involved in the selection of and to vote for civil rulers who fear God, love truth and justice, hate evil, and are publicly committed to scriptural principles of civil government.
Ex. 18:21; Deut. 16:18; 2 Sam. 23:3; Rom. 13:3.

16. It is sinful for a Christian to take an oath which compromises his supreme allegiance to Jesus Christ. It is also sinful to vote for officials who are required to take an oath which a Christian himself could not take in good conscience. Voting involves the voter in responsibility for any act required of the official as a condition of holding his office.
Deut. 10:20; Isa. 45:22-23; 2 John 1:11; 1 Tim. 5:22.

17. The Christian must profess publicly and the Church must witness, that Christ is the Ruler of every nation. Whatever the official action of the civil government of a nation may be, the Christian in his civil actions must always exhibit his loyalty to Christ. The Christian must relinquish every right or privilege of citizenship which involves him in silence about, or denial of the supreme authority of Jesus Christ.
Matt. 5:13-14; Prov. 3:5-6; Ps. 37:7; Matt. 22:21; John 17:14-15; Mark 13:9.

3. The civil magistrate may not assume to himself the administration of the Word and sacraments, or the power of the keys of the kingdom of heaven: yet he hath authority, and it is his duty, to take order, that unity and peace be preserved in the Church, that the truth of God be kept pure and entire; that

18. *We reject* the portion of paragraph 3 after the colon.

all blasphemies and heresies be suppressed; all corruptions and abuses in worship and discipline prevented or reformed; and all the ordinances of God duly settled, administered and observed. For the better effecting whereof, he hath power to call synods, to be present at them, and to provide, that whatsoever is transacted in them be according to the mind of God.

2 Chron. 26:18 with Matt. 18:17 and Matt. 16:19; 1 Cor. 12:28-29; Eph. 4:11-12; 1 Cor. 4:1-2; Rom. 10:15; Heb. 5:4; Isa. 49:23; Ps. 122:9; Ezra 7:23, 25-28; Lev. 24:16; Deut. 13:5-6, 12; 1 Kings 18:4; 1 Chron. 13:1-9; 2 Kings 23:1-26; 2 Chron. 34:33; 2 Chron. 15:12-13; 2 Chron. 19:8-11; 2 Chron. 29—30; Matt. 2:4-5.

19. Both the government of the nation and the government of the visible church are established by God. Though distinct and independent of each other, they both owe supreme allegiance to Jesus Christ. The governments of church and state differ in sphere of authority in that due submission to the government of the visible church is the obligation of members thereof, while due submission to civil government is the obligation of all men. The governments of church and state also have different functions and prerogatives in the advancement of the Kingdom of God. The means of enforcement of the civil government are physical, while those of church government are not. Neither government has the right to invade or assume the authority of the other. They should cooperate to the honor and glory of God, while maintaining their separate jurisdictions.

Rom. 13:1; Matt. 22:21; Col. 1:18; Acts 15:10; Ezra 7:10, 25-26; 2 Chron. 26:18-19; Matt. 5:25; 1 Cor. 5:12-13.

20. Though responsible for maintaining conditions favorable to the spread of the Gospel, civil government should never attempt to convert men to Christ by the use of force or by persecution. It should guarantee to all its subjects every human right given by God to men. It should, however, restrain and punish its subjects for those sinful actions which fall under its jurisdiction.

1 Tim. 2:1-4; 1 Pet. 2:13-14; Rom. 13:4; Ezra 7:26; Neh. 13: 17-21.

4. It is the duty of people to pray for magistrates, to honour their persons, to pay them tribute and other dues, to obey their lawful commands, and to be subject to their authority, for conscience' sake. Infidelity, or difference in religion, doth not make void the magistrates' just and legal authority, nor free the people from their due obedience to them: from which ecclesiastical persons are not exempted; much less hath the Pope any power and jurisdiction over them in their dominions, or over any of their people; and, least of all, to deprive them of their dominions, or lives, if he shall judge them to be heretics, or upon any other pretence whatsoever.

1 Tim. 2:1-2; 1 Pet. 2:17; Rom. 13:6-7; Rom. 13:5; Titus 3:1; 1 Pet. 2:13-14, 16; Rom. 13:1; 1 Kings 2:35; Acts 25:9-11; 2 Pet. 2: 1, 10-11; Jude 1:8-11; 2 Thess. 2:4; Rev. 13:15-17.

21. No civil government which deprives men of civil or religious liberty, fails to protect human life, or proposes to force men to do violence to the spirit and precepts of the Christian religion or interferes unjustly with private ownership of property, can in such matters rightfully expect the submission of its citizens or the blessings of God promised for obedience to Him.

Acts 4:17, 19, 33; Deut. 27:19; Isa. 10:1-2; Ex. 20:15; Isa. 1:23-26; Dan. 6:13; Heb. 11:23.

22. Both the Christian and the Church have a responsibility for witnessing against national sins and for promoting justice.

Amos 2:6-8; Amos 5:14-15.

23. The failure of a civil government, through negligence, ignorance, or rebellion, to recognize the authority of Jesus Christ does not cancel its just authority. A civil government, though guilty of many sins, still has authority in so far as it furthers some of the scriptural ends of civil government.

Matt. 22:21; Rom. 13:1; Rom. 2:14; Acts 23:5; Ex. 22:28.

24. Due submission of all persons, cheerfully rendered, to civil officers and to civil government in general, is pleasing to God. No person, however, is required by God to obey civil authority when such authority demands that the citizen or subject do that which is clearly contrary to the law of God as revealed in the Scriptures. In such cases the duty of the Christian is to obey God rather than men. The Christian has a special obligation to render due submission to civil authority in order to express his loyalty to Jesus Christ, to prove his concern for the welfare of all men, and to bring honor to the name of Christ.
1 Pet. 2:13-14; Rom. 13:5; Acts 5:29; Titus 3:1.

25. The only submission which a Christian may promise to any civil government is due submission in the Lord. Any promise of submission or oath of allegiance beyond this is sinful. If and when the civil government of a nation requires, as a condition of civil service or of holding office, an oath which implies that civil allegiance transcends the swearer's convictions of conscience and obedience to God, it is the Christian's duty to refuse such an oath. It is within the corporate power of the Church, acting through its courts, to declare that facts or circumstances which may exist in a specific situation render the taking of a civil oath sinful.
Gen. 25:33; Matt. 22:21; Eph. 6:12; Matt. 4:10; Deut. 10:20.

26. It is the duty of the Christian to ascertain whether any prescribed oath of allegiance to the civil authority involves acceptance of unchristian principles stated or implied in its constitution of government. If the oath of allegiance to civil authority explicitly or by clear implication requires support of anti-Christian, atheistic, or secular principles, then the Christian must refuse on these grounds to take the oath of allegiance.
Acts 5:29; Acts 4:18-20.

27. In the matter of taking oaths required by civil authority, the Christian should seek the guidance and support of the Church.

28. It is the duty of the Christian Church to testify to the authority of Christ over the nations, against all anti-Christian, atheistic, and secular principles of civil government, and against all sinful oaths of allegiance to civil governments. When the Church by orderly processes in her own courts determines that the oath of allegiance to a civil government compromises the Christian's loyalty to Christ or involves the Christian in the support of sinful principles of civil government, the Church must require her members to refuse such sinful oaths.
Acts 4:24-29; Eph. 5:11; Rev. 3:15-16; Acts 15:28-29; Rev. 2:13-14.

29. When participating in political elections, the Christian should support and vote only for such men as are publicly committed to scriptural principles of civil government. Should the Christian seek civil office by political election, he must openly inform those whose support he seeks of his adherence to Christian principles of civil government.
1 Chron. 16:31; 2 Cor. 6:14-18; 2 Chron. 19:6-7; Dan. 2:48; Eph. 4:25.

30. God alone is Lord of the conscience, and the decisions of civil courts cannot determine for the Christian what is morally right and what is sinful. However, since civil government is an institution of God, it is within the legitimate province of the civil courts of a nation to determine what the nation's laws and required oaths of allegiance mean or do not mean. A decision of a civil court cannot legitimize sinful conduct, but it can place before a Christian a factual situation upon which a moral judgment can be made. It cannot be proper for the Christian to assume that an oath of allegiance implies sinful requirements, when the civil courts have explicitly contradicted such implication. Every oath must be understood in the sense intended by the authority requiring the oath. It is for the Christian and the Church to decide whether this sense involves sinful requirements.
Matt. 22:21b; Rom. 13:5; Eccl. 8:4; 1 Thess. 5:21.

31. *We reject* any inference that civil government has jurisdiction over conscience.

Chapter 24: Of Marriage and Divorce

(Larger Catechism: 137-139; Shorter Catechism: 63-66, 70-72)
(The *Testimony* also treats "Education of Children" in this chapter.)

1. Marriage is an ordinance of God; however, to be unmarried is also an equally honorable state, and it may be the will of God for a person to remain single. Every effort should be made to submit to the direction of God in this matter, and to maintain a chaste and obedient life style.
1 Cor. 7:7-8.

2. Premarital sex relations or promiscuous sex practices as well as homosexuality and other perversions of the natural order are violations of God's law and purpose. All should strive to discipline their sexual desires, maintain purity of thought and practice, and avoid situations which lead to sexual temptation.
1 Cor. 6:9, 15-20; 1 Cor. 5:1-5, 9-11; 1 Cor. 7:8-9; Rom. 1:26-28; Phil. 4:8; Prov. 5.

1. Marriage is to be between one man and one woman: neither is it lawful for any man to have more than one wife, nor for any woman to have more than one husband; at the same time.
Gen. 2:24; Matt. 19:5-6; Prov. 2:17.

3. By God's appointment the marriage relationship is to continue as long as both parties are living. Marriage may not be contracted for any other period. After the death of one party the other party may lawfully marry another.
Matt. 19:4-6; Rom. 7:2-3; Gen. 2:24-25; 1 Cor. 7:39.

4. Marriage is a covenant relationship made before God between a man and a woman.
Prov. 2:17; Mal. 2:14; cf. Hos. 2:16-23.

5. The validity of marriage depends on the mutual agreement of the parties, rather than upon official administration; yet for the glory of God and the protection of the parties, and so that the greatness of the privilege and the seriousness of the responsibility of the marriage may be properly impressed on the parties, marriage should be contracted in the presence of a qualified officer and competent witnesses.
Matt. 19:6; 1 Cor. 10:31; 1 Pet. 2:13.

6. The marriage of Christians should ordinarily be solemnized by an ordained minister of the Gospel.
1 Cor. 14:33, 40.

7. Parties to marriage should comply with the civil laws regarding marriage as long as these laws are not contrary to Scripture.
1 Pet. 2:13.

2. Marriage was ordained for the mutual help of husband and wife, for the increase of mankind with a legitimate issue, and of the Church with an holy seed; and for preventing of uncleanness.
Gen. 2:18; Mal. 2:15; 1 Cor. 7:2, 9.

8. God created man, male and female, with specific responsibilities to each other.
Gen. 2:18-25.

9. As sexual beings, men and women are, in ordinary circumstances, to marry for the expression of love, the satisfaction of their needs, and the mutual enjoyment of each other, as well as the continuation of the race.
1 Cor. 7:3-5.

10. God has ordained a natural order within the family: the husband is the head of the family, having a relationship to his wife like that of Christ to the Church. He is ordinarily the provider for his family. He is to love his wife as Christ loves His Church and as his own body. He is to love, discipline and instruct his children, and to lead his family in worship.
1 Tim. 5:8; Eph. 5:25-28; 1 Pet. 3:7; Prov. 19:18; Prov. 22:6; Eph. 6:4; Deut. 6:4-9.

11. The wife is to be a helper to her husband. The Scripture commands submission to her husband in the Lord. She is to join her husband in the wise use of family resources, the care and instruction of children and the maintenance of the home as a place of love, cheerfulness and hospitality.

Gen. 2:18; Eph. 5:22-24; Prov. 31:10-31; 1 Pet. 3:1, 6.

12. Children are commanded to obey and honor their parents in the Lord.
Ex. 20:12; Deut. 5:16; Eph. 6:1-3.

13. Family administration involves mutual responsibility. The exchange or confusion of roles in the family in ordinary circumstances results in God's displeasure and in consequent unhappiness.
Eph. 5:22; Eph. 6:4; Ps. 128; Col. 3:18-21.

14. *We deny* that the submission in the Lord of a wife to her husband contradicts the equality, in value and dignity, of her person to his.
Gen. 1:27; Gal. 3:28.

15. While we abhor the sinful abuses of a husband's authority and the abdication of his responsibilities within marriage, common since the Fall, *we deny* that his headship is, in and of itself, a result of sin.
Gen. 2:18; 1 Cor. 11:3-10; Eph. 5:23; 1 Tim. 2:11-13.

16. Although in certain circumstances in the service of God it may be unwise for a person to marry, we deny that Scripture forbids officers of the Church to marry.
1 Cor. 9:5; 1 Tim. 4:3.

17. *We deny* that marriage is a more spiritual state than the single life, or that it is necessary for eternal salvation.
1 Cor. 7:7-8.

18. *We deny* that marriage is necessary for officers in the Church.
1 Cor. 7:7.

19. Unborn children are living creatures in the image of God. From the moment of conception to birth they are objects of God's providence as they are being prepared by Him for the responsibilities and privileges of postnatal life. Unborn children are to be treated as human persons in all decisions and actions involving them. Deliberately induced abortion, except possibly to save the mother's life, is murder.
Ex. 20:13; Ex. 21:22-23; Ps. 139:13-16.

3. It is lawful for all sorts of people to marry, who are able with judgment to give their consent. Yet is it the duty of Christians to marry only in the Lord: and therefore such as profess the true reformed religion should not marry with infidels, papists, or other idolaters: neither should such as are godly be unequally yoked, by marrying with such as are notoriously wicked in their life, or maintain damnable heresies.

20. Christians should not marry those who give only nominal adherence to the Christian faith.
1 Cor. 7:39; 2 Cor. 6:14.

Heb. 13:4; 1 Tim. 4:3; 1 Cor. 7:36-38; Gen. 24:57-58; 1 Cor. 7:39; Gen. 34:14; Ex. 34:16; Deut. 7:3-4; 1 Kings 11:4; Neh. 13:25-27; Mal. 2:11-12; 2 Cor. 6:14.

4. Marriage ought not to be within the degrees of consanguinity or affinity forbidden in the Word; nor can such incestuous marriages ever be made lawful by any law of man or consent of parties, so as those persons may live together as man and wife. The man may not marry any of his wife's kindred nearer in blood than he may of his own; nor the woman of her husband's kindred nearer in blood than of her own.
Lev. 18; 1 Cor. 5:1; Amos 2:7; Mark 6:18; Lev. 18:24-28; Lev. 20:19-21.

5. Adultery or fornication committed after a contract, being detected before marriage, giveth just occasion to the innocent party to dissolve that contract. In the case of adultery after marriage, it is lawful for the innocent party to sue out a divorce; and, after the divorce, to marry another, as if the offending party were dead.
Matt. 1:18-20; Matt. 5:31-32; Matt. 19:9; Rom. 7:2-3.

6. Although the corruption of man be such as is apt to study arguments unduly to put asunder those whom God hath joined together in marriage; yet nothing but adultery, or such wilful desertion as can no way be remedied by the Church or civil magistrate, is cause sufficient of dissolving the bond of marriage; wherein, a public and orderly course of proceeding is to be observed; and the persons concerned in it not left to their own wills and discretion, in their own case.
Matt. 19:8-9; 1 Cor. 7:15; Matt. 19:6; Deut. 24:1-4.

21. *We reject* the last sentence in paragraph 4 of the *Confession of Faith*.

22. The prohibition of marriage with a deceased wife's sister or a deceased husband's brother is not warranted by Scripture.
Lev. 18:18; Deut. 25:5-10.

23. Before seeking divorce, it is the responsibility of the innocent party to attempt reconciliation with the guilty party in the same manner as in any case of sin, first by his or her own appeal, and then, if need be, by calling on the elders of the church.
Matt. 18:15-17.

24. In any marriage threatened with dissolution, or even if divorce has occurred, both parties ought to strive for reconciliation on the basis of repentance for sin and willingness to forgive.
Eph. 5:25-33; Eph. 4:31-32; 1 Cor. 7:10-14.

25. Members of the household of faith should beware of seeking marriage counsel from unbelievers or from those who have failed to integrate their faith with their professional work.
Matt. 18:15-17; 2 Cor. 6:14-17.

26. Desertion can be a ground of divorce only when the departing person is an unbeliever.
1 Cor. 7:15; Matt. 18:17.

27. If the unrepentant guilty party in a divorce marries another, he commits adultery.
Matt. 19:9.

28. Where the guilty party shows evidence of repentance for the sin of breaking a marriage, the Church may receive or restore him or her to membership.
Gal. 6:1.

Education of Children

29. God is the source of all truth. The knowledge which man can attain merely reflects part of God's creation, and cannot properly be understood apart from God. Therefore

there can be no true education without a knowledge of God and His dealings with man, as revealed in the Scriptures. He enlightens man's mind in the understanding of the physical and cultural world. Christians are to ask the aid of the Holy Spirit in the educational task.
Ps. 24:1; Ps. 111:10; Prov. 2:6; Prov. 9:10; Ex. 31:3-6.

30. Education of children is primarily the responsibility of parents, though they may delegate part of this responsibility to the church or other agencies. The earliest and most important educational institution is the home, where children are taught, by precept and example, basic principles of godly living. Parents should educate each child to the extent of their resources and the child's ability, seeking to develop his God-given talents that he may serve God most fully and effectively. In order to promote the general welfare, the state may prescribe educational standards and should provide educational opportunities, both in harmony with God's law.
Deut. 6:6-9; Ps. 34:11; Ps. 78:2-7; Prov. 22:6.

31. In the providence of God public schools have provided great social benefits. Yet in serving a highly pluralistic society they have attempted to be religiously and morally "neutral," which is sinful. To a large extent instruction is based on a secular, humanistic philosophy which ignores God and sees man's welfare as the highest good. Local schools vary widely, however, according to the standards of the community and the quality of the teachers. All Christians, especially those who are teachers, school administrators or board members, should bear witness to the whole truth of God as it relates to education.
Matt. 12:30; 2 Sam. 23:3-4.

32. Where necessary and possible, Christian parents should cooperate in supporting or establishing schools whose curriculum presents a biblical world and life view, and place their children in them. This requires maintenance of the highest academic quality along with Christian orientation in every subject and activity.

33. *We reject* any attempt by the state to force a secular, humanistic philosophy on Christian schools.

34. Parents should take care to counteract any unbiblical teaching given to their children, whether in public or Christian schools. As youth increase in their knowledge and discernment, the home and the Church should help them to examine what is presented in school, to distinguish between God-given truths and human theories, and to integrate the facts learned with a Christian view of man and the universe.
Isa. 8:20.

Chapter 25: Of the Church

(Larger Catechism: 60-65)

1. The catholic or universal Church which is invisible, consists of the whole number of the elect, that have been, are, or shall be gathered into one, under Christ the Head thereof; and is the spouse, the body, the fulness of Him that filleth all in all.
Eph. 1:10, 22-23; Eph. 5:23, 27, 32; Col. 1:18.

1. The Church is the body of Christ, which He has redeemed with His own blood, to be a chosen people unto Himself.

2. It is the mission of the Church to preserve, maintain and proclaim to the whole world the Gospel of Jesus Christ and the whole counsel of God; to gather into her fellowship those of every race and people who accept Jesus Christ as Savior and Lord, and promise obedience to Him; to build them up in their most holy faith, and train them to be faithful witnesses for Christ in all his offices; to maintain the ordinances of divine worship in their purity; witness against all evil; and in every way to seek the advancement of the Kingdom of God on earth.

2. The visible Church, which is also catholic or universal under the Gospel (not confined to one nation as before under the law), consists of all those throughout the world that profess the true religion; and of their children: and is the kingdom of the Lord Jesus Christ, the house and family of God, out of which there is no ordinary possibility of salvation.
1 Cor. 1:2; 1 Cor. 12:12-13; Ps. 2:8; Rev. 7:9; Rom. 15:9-12; 1 Cor. 7:14; Acts 2:39; Ezek. 16:20-21; Rom. 11:16; Gen. 3:15; Gen. 17:7; Matt. 13:47; Isa. 9:7; Eph. 2:19; Eph. 3:15; Acts 2:47.

3. The Church is one among all nations, yet for the purpose of corporate worship and orderly procedures, distinct congregations and judicatories are warranted.
Acts 15:22; Acts 16:4-5; 1 Cor. 1:2; Gal. 1:2; Phil. 1:1; Col. 4:15-16.

4. There is a visible and an invisible aspect of the Church, but these are not two churches.
Heb. 12:23; Rev. 3:1, 5.

5. *We reject* the teaching that the Church originated in the New Testament and is an interruption of God's plan for the Kingdom.
Rom. 11:17-24; Heb. 9:13-10:18.

3. Unto this catholic visible Church Christ hath given the ministry, oracles, and ordinances of God, for the gathering and perfecting of the saints, in this life, to the end of the world; and doth by His own presence and Spirit, according to His promise, make them effectual thereunto.
1 Cor. 12:28; Eph. 4:11-13; Matt. 28:19-20; Isa. 59:21.

6. The Lord Jesus Christ has clothed His Church with power and authority. This authority is vested in the whole membership of the Church, which has the right to choose its officers from among those of its own members who possess the scriptural qualifications.

7. Christ has appointed in His Word a particular form of government for the visible church. It is government by elders (Greek: presbyters) and is therefore called presbyterian. Each congregation should be ruled by a session of ordained elders, elected by the membership of the congregation.
Acts 15:22; Acts 14:23; Acts 13:1-4; Eph. 5:23; Col. 1:18; 2 Cor. 8:19; 1 Tim. 3:1-7. (See *Testimony*, chap. 31, par. 3; and *Directory for Church Government,* chap. 3, sect. I and II, and chap. 4.)

8. The permanent officers to be set apart by ordination are elders and deacons. The office of elder is restricted in Scripture to men. Women as well as men may hold the office of

deacon. Ordination is a solemn setting apart to a specific office by the laying on of the hands of a court of the Church and is not to be repeated. Installation is the official constitution of a relationship between one who is ordained and the congregation.
1 Tim. 2:12; 3:2; Titus 1:6.

9. The responsibility of the elders is in teaching and ruling. Although all elders are to be able to teach, the Scripture recognizes a distinction in these functions. All elders are equal in the government of the Church. This office is referred to in Scripture by two terms used synonymously: elder, and bishop or overseer.
1 Tim. 3:2; Titus 1:9; 1 Tim. 5:17; Acts 20:28; Rom. 12:6-8; 1 Cor. 12:28; Titus 1:7.

10. The elders are organized in courts (the session, the presbytery and the Synod) to which is committed the power of governing the church and of ordaining officers. This power is moral and spiritual, and subject to the law of God.
Eph. 4:11-12; 1 Tim 3:2; Titus 1:9; 1 Tim. 5:17; Acts 20:28; Rom. 12:6-8; 1 Cor 12:28; Titus 1:7.

11. The diaconate is a spiritual office subordinate to the session and is not a teaching or ruling office. The deacons have responsibility for the ministry of mercy, the finances and property of the congregation, and such other tasks as are assigned to them by the session. Other officers mentioned in the New Testament were commissioned uniquely during the apostolic age for the establishment of the Church.
Acts 6:1-7; 1 Tim. 3:8-13.

12. While the New Testament does not state plainly the authority or qualifications for a continuing office of Evangelist, it does clearly set forth the ministry of evangelism in calling all men everywhere to repent and believe the Gospel. Persons displaying the gift of evangelism should minister under the oversight of the Church in given situations.

13. *We deny* that the exclusion of women from the office of elder can be said to result in the frustration of one's divine vocation or the neglect of one's spiritual gifts for ministry.
1 Cor. 12:14-26.

14. Divisions that separate believers into denominations mar the unity of the Church and are due to error and sin. It is the duty of all denominations which are true churches of Christ to seek reconciliation and union. Such organizational unity, however, should be sought only on the basis of truth and of scriptural order. It is the duty of every believer to unite with the branch of the visible church which adheres most closely to the Scriptures.

4. This catholic Church hath been sometimes more, sometimes less visible. And particular churches, which are members thereof, are more or less pure, according as the doctrine of the Gospel is taught and embraced, ordinances administered, and public worship performed more or less purely in them.
Rom. 11:3-4; Rev. 12:6, 14; Rev. 2-3; 1 Cor. 5:6-7.

Acts 15:22-29; 1 Cor. 10:17; Eph. 4:4-6; Acts 17:11-12.

15. The Church must have membership requirements based on Scripture, to which every member gives his assent. Those who give such assent and their children are church members. Acts 2:39; 1 Cor. 7:14; Rev. 2–3. (See *Directory for Church Government,* chap. 1, sect. I.)

16. It is the duty of Christians to pray for and seek after the purity and unity of the Church. Ps. 122:6-9; John 17:11, 21; Eph. 4:13.

17. When any church imposes sinful requirements for membership; when its constitution or creedal statements are fundamentally unscriptural; when its administration is corrupt; or when sound preaching and proper discipline are neglected, it is the duty of Christians to attempt its reformation. Then if such efforts prove ineffectual, it is their duty to separate from it, and to unite with a sound church. Rev. 2:20-23; Acts 19:8-9; 2 Cor. 6:16-17.

18. Many antichrists will be present in the world throughout history. Prior to Christ's coming the final "man of lawlessness" will be revealed. He will be destroyed by Christ. 1 John 2:18; 1 John 4:3; 2 Thess. 2:8.

19. Christians should walk in the light. Their beliefs, purposes, manner of life, and their rules of action and conduct should be based on the Word of God and should not be concealed. Oathbound societies usually involve an improper requirement of secrecy, aims which are immoral, intimate fellowship with unbelievers or participation in unbiblical worship. Membership in such organizations is inconsistent with a Christian profession, however good their announced purposes may be. 1 John 1:7; 1 Thess. 5:5; Matt. 5:14; 2 John 1:7-11; John 3:20-21; Eph. 5:8-14; Matt. 15:9.

5. The purest churches under heaven are subject both to mixture and error; and some have so degenerated, as to become no churches of Christ, but synagogues of Satan. Nevertheless, there shall be always a Church on earth, to worship God according to His will. 1 Cor. 13:12; Rev. 2–3; Matt. 13:24-30, 47; Rev. 18:2; Rom. 11:18-22; Matt. 16:18; Ps. 72:17; Ps. 102:28; Matt. 28:19-20.

6. There is no other head of the Church, but the Lord Jesus Christ; nor can the Pope of Rome, in any sense, be head thereof; but is that Antichrist, that man of sin, and son of perdition, that exalteth himself, in the Church, against Christ and all that is called God. Col. 1:18; Eph. 1:22; Matt. 23:8-10; 2 Thess. 2:3-4, 8-9; Rev. 13:6.

Chapter 26: Of the Communion of Saints

(Larger Catechism: 135-136, 141-142; Shorter Catechism: 68-69, 74-81)

1. All saints, that are united to Jesus Christ their Head by His Spirit and by faith, have fellowship with Him in His graces, sufferings, death, resurrection, and glory: and, being united to one another in love, they have communion in each other's gifts and graces, and are obliged to the performance of such duties, public and private, as do conduce to their mutual good, both in the inward and outward man. 1 John 1:3; Eph. 3:16-19; John 1:16; Eph. 2:5-6; Phil. 3:10; Rom. 6:5-6; 2 Tim. 2:12; Eph. 4:15-16; 1 Cor. 12:7; 1 Cor. 3:

1. Concern for fellow believers should be a restraint to evil, especially to unkind speech and action against one another. 1 Cor. 13; Eph. 4:31-32; Rom. 14:19; Jas. 3:16-18; Gal. 5:15; 1 Cor. 12.

21-23; Col. 2:19; 1 Thess. 5:11, 14; Rom. 1:11-12, 14; 1 John 3: 16-18; Gal. 6:10.

2. Saints by profession are bound to maintain a holy fellowship and communion in the worship of God; and in performing such other spiritual services as tend to their mutual edification; as also in relieving each other in outward things, according to their several abilities, and necessities. Which communion, as God offereth opportunity, is to be extended unto all those who, in every place, call upon the name of the Lord Jesus.
Heb. 10:24-25; Acts 2:42, 46; Isa. 2:3; 1 Cor. 11:20; Acts 2:44-45; 1 John 3:17; 2 Cor. 8—9; Acts 11:29-30.

2. The congregation is the primary organic unit in the presbyterian system of church government. It is commonly composed of Christians residing in the same community who meet together for the worship of God.

3. In addition to their obligation to assemble for worship, believers should assemble for social purposes as another means of support and growth. In response to Christ's love for them, believers are to express their love to one another by using their diverse gifts and talents to help their brethren; by giving and receiving counsel, support, hospitality and comfort; by spending time with one another and sharing joys and sorrows. This is especially necessary when, in the providence of God, brethren need material support and moral and spiritual encouragement.
Heb. 10:24-25; Heb. 13:2; Gal. 6:2; Rom. 12:10, 13, 15; Eph. 4: 28; Phil. 4:10-14; 1 Cor. 16:1-2.

4. For preservation of life and because of respect for our bodies as God's creation, we are to be careful in the use of drugs. Christians should avoid enslavement to alcohol, tobacco or any habit-forming drug. The Scripture strongly condemns drunkenness as a sin.
Gen. 1:27 with 9:6; 1 Cor. 6:9-10.

5. Because drunkenness is so common, and because the intemperate use of alcohol is constantly being promoted by advertising, business practices, and social pressure, Christians must be careful not to conform to the attitudes and the practices of the world with regard to alcoholic beverages. To prevent damage to our neighbor, to provide mutual help in godly living, and to strengthen each other in living a disciplined life it is altogether wise and proper that Christians refrain from the use, sale and manufacture of alcoholic beverages.
Prov. 20:1; Rom. 14:21; 1 Cor. 6:9-10; 1 Cor. 8:13.

6. The use of tobacco is detrimental to health and is to be avoided because of the responsibility to preserve the body which is a temple of God.
1 Cor. 6:19; 1 Cor. 9:24-27.

7. The use of drugs for pleasure or escape from moral responsibility should be avoided; one should strive for victory over physical and emotional weakness through the strength of Christ and the power of the Holy Spirit, and make wise use of proper medical care.
Phil. 4:13; Col. 1:10-14.

3. This communion, which the saints have with Christ, doth not make them, in any wise, partakers of the substance of His Godhead; or to be equal with Christ, in any respect: either of which to affirm is impious and blasphemous. Nor doth their communion one with another, as saints, take away, or infringe the title or property which each man hath in his goods and possessions.
Col. 1:18-19; 1 Cor. 8:6; Isa. 42:8; 1 Tim. 6:15-16; Ps. 45:7 with Heb. 1:8-9; Ex. 20:15; Eph. 4:28; Acts 5:4.

Chapter 27: Of the Sacraments

(Larger Catechism: 161-177; Shorter Catechism: 91-97)

1. Sacraments are holy signs and seals of the covenant of grace, immediately instituted by God, to represent Christ and His benefits; and to confirm our interest in Him; as also, to put a visible difference between those that belong unto the Church, and the rest of the world; and solemnly to engage them to the service of God in Christ, according to His Word.
Rom. 4:11; Gen. 17:7, 10; Matt. 28:19; 1 Cor. 11:23; 1 Cor. 10:16; 1 Cor. 11:25-26; Gal. 3:17; Rom. 15:8; Ex. 12:48; Gen. 34:14; Rom. 6:3-4; 1 Cor. 10:16, 21.

2. There is in every sacrament a spiritual relation, or sacramental union, between the sign and the thing signified; whence it comes to pass, that the names and effects of the one are attributed to the other.
Gen. 17:10; Matt. 26:27-28; Titus 3:5.

3. The grace which is exhibited in or by the sacraments rightly used, is not conferred by any power in them: neither doth the efficacy of a sacrament depend upon the piety or intention of him that doth administer it: but upon the work of the Spirit, and the word of institution, which contains, together with a precept authorizing the use thereof, a promise of benefit to worthy receivers.
Rom. 2:28-29; 1 Pet. 3:21; Matt. 3:11; 1 Cor. 12:13; Matt. 26: 27-28; Matt. 28:19-20.

4. There be only two sacraments ordained by Christ our Lord in the Gospel; that is to say, Baptism and the Supper of the Lord: neither of which may be dispensed by any but by a minister of the Word lawfully ordained.
Matt. 28:19; 1 Cor. 11:20, 23; 1 Cor. 4:1; Heb. 5:4.

5. The sacraments of the Old Testament, in regard of the spiritual things thereby signified and exhibited, were, for substance, the same with those of the New.
1 Cor. 10:1-4.

1. The sacraments are signs of our covenant union with Christ and His Church, and our common profession that we are owned by Him. They are to be observed under the direction of the elders in a service of worship in which members of the congregation are present.
1 Cor. 11:23-24; 1 Cor. 10:21; Acts 2:42; Num. 9:14.

2. The administration of the sacraments is to be accompanied by the reading and preaching of the Word.
Acts 2:42; Acts 20:7.

3. *We reject* the view that sacraments are mere symbols and not means of grace.

4. *We reject* the view that the sacraments are not necessary in the Church.

Chapter 28: Of Baptism

(Larger Catechism: 161-177; Shorter Catechism: 92-95)

1. Baptism is a sacrament of the New Testament, ordained by Jesus Christ, not only for the solemn admission of the party baptized into the visible Church; but also, to be unto him a sign and seal of the covenant of grace, of his ingrafting into Christ, of regeneration, of remission of sins, and of his giving up unto God through Jesus Christ, to walk in newness of

1. All those who have received baptism are to be considered part of the covenant people of God.
Gen. 17:12-14; Col. 2:11-12; Acts 16:31-34.

life. Which sacrament is, by Christ's own appointment, to be continued in His Church until the end of the world.
Matt. 28:19; 1 Cor. 12:13; Rom. 4:11 with Col. 2:11-12; Gal. 3:27; Rom. 6:5; Titus 3:5; Mark 1:4; Rom. 6:3-4; Matt. 28:19-20.

2. The outward element to be used in this sacrament is water, wherewith the party is to be baptized, in the name of the Father, and of the Son, and of the Holy Ghost, by a minister of the Gospel, lawfully called thereunto.
Matt. 3:11; John 1:33; Matt. 28:19-20.

3. Dipping of the person into the water is not necessary; but Baptism is rightly administered by pouring or sprinkling water upon the person.
Heb. 9:10, 19-22; Acts 2:41; Acts 16:33; Mark 7:4.

4. Not only those that do actually profess faith in and obedience unto Christ, but also the infants of one or both believing parents, are to be baptized.
Mark 16:15-16; Acts 8:37-38; Gen. 17:7, 9-10 with Gal. 3:9, 14, and Col. 2:11-12, and Acts 2:38-39, and Rom. 4:11-12; 1 Cor. 7:14; Matt. 28:19; Mark 10:13-16; Luke 18:15.

5. Although it be a great sin to contemn or neglect this ordinance, yet grace and salvation are not so inseparably annexed unto it, as that no person can be regenerated or saved without it; or, that all that are baptized are undoubtedly regenerated.
Luke 7:30 with Ex. 4:24-26; Rom. 4:11; Acts 10:2, 4, 22, 31, 45, 47; Acts 8:13, 23.

6. The efficacy of Baptism is not tied to that moment of time wherein it is administered; yet notwithstanding, by the right use of this ordinance, the grace promised is not only offered, but really exhibited and conferred by the Holy Ghost, to such (whether of age or infants) as that grace belongeth unto, according to the counsel of God's own will in His appointed time.

2. The church accepts as valid the baptism which has been administered in any true branch of the visible church.

3. *We reject* the teaching that an essential feature of baptism is immersion.
1 Cor. 10:2; Heb. 6:2; Heb. 9:10; Luke 11:38.

4. The children of believing parents are to receive baptism because of their covenantal relationship.
Acts 2:38-39; Gen. 17:7; Acts 16:31; Col. 2:11-12.

5. In administering baptism to her children the church recognizes their rightful place within the covenant, and her obligation to give them pastoral care and oversight, and to assist the parents in carrying out their covenanted responsibilities. In presenting them for baptism, parents not only claim for their children the nurture and benefits of the Church, but dedicate them to God in the service of Christ.

6. The baptism of infants sets before parents the obligation to do all in their power to lead their children to a personal faith in Jesus Christ.
Gen. 18:19; Matt. 28:19-20; Prov. 22:6.

7. Baptism is not to be administered to the infants of persons who, though members of the church, have so neglected the means of grace as to cast doubt on their profession, or their intention to fulfill the baptismal vows.
Ps. 76:11.

8. *We reject* the teaching that a person cannot be saved without baptism; or that persons are regenerated by baptism.
Luke 23:39-43; Acts 8:13, 18-23; Acts 10:47.

John 3:5, 8; Gal. 3:27; Titus 3:5; Eph. 5:25-26; Acts 2:38, 41.

7. The sacrament of Baptism is but once to be administered unto any person.
Titus 3:5.

Chapter 29: Of the Lord's Supper

(Larger Catechism: 168-177; Shorter Catechism: 92-93, 96-97)

1. Our Lord Jesus, in the night wherein He was betrayed, instituted the sacrament of His body and blood, called the Lord's Supper, to be observed in His Church, unto the end of the world, for the perpetual remembrance of the sacrifice of Himself in His death; the sealing all benefits thereof unto true believers, their spiritual nourishment and growth in Him, their further engagement in and to all duties which they owe unto Him; and to be a bond and pledge of their communion with Him, and with each other, as members of His mystical body.
1 Cor. 11:23-26; 1 Cor. 10:16-17, 21; 1 Cor. 12:13.

1. The Lord's Supper is to be repeatedly administered to a Christian congregation, at such times as the session deems advisable, according to the needs of the congregation. Observance of this sacrament is a corporate and personal profession of continued adherence to the covenant bond entered into at baptism.
1 Cor. 11:23-26.

2. In this sacrament, Christ is not offered up to His Father; nor any real sacrifice made at all for remission of sins of the quick or dead; but only a commemoration of that one offering up of Himself, by Himself, upon the cross, once for all: and a spiritual oblation of all possible praise unto God for the same: so that the Popish sacrifice of the mass (as they call it) is most abominably injurious to Christ's one, only sacrifice, the alone propitiation for all the sins of His elect.
Heb. 9:22, 25-26, 28; 1 Cor. 11:24-26; Matt. 26:26-27; Heb. 7: 23-24, 27; Heb. 10:11-12, 14, 18.

3. The Lord Jesus, hath, in this ordinance, appointed His ministers to declare His word of institution to the people; to pray, and bless the elements of bread and wine, and thereby to set them apart from a common to a holy use; and to take and break the bread, to take the cup, and (they communicating also themselves) to give both to the communicants; but to none who are not then present in the congregation.
Matt. 26:26-28, and Mark 14:22-24, and Luke 22:19-20 with 1 Cor. 11:23-26; Acts 20:7; 1 Cor. 11:20.

4. Private masses, or receiving this sacrament by a priest or any other alone; as likewise, the denial of the cup to the people, worshipping the elements, the lifting them up or carrying them about for adoration, and the reserving them for any pretended religious use; are all contrary to the nature of this sacrament, and to the institution of Christ.
1 Cor. 10:16; Mark 14:23; 1 Cor. 11:25-29; Matt. 15:9.

2. When a congregation is observing the Lord's Supper, worship services in which this sacrament is observed may be held for the sick and invalid who are of sound mind in the presence of members of the session and congregation. There is no instance in Scripture of private communion.
1 Cor. 11:33; Acts 20:7.

3. The sacrament of the Lord's Supper is not to be exalted above the regular preaching of the Word.

5. The outward elements in this sacrament, duly set apart to the uses ordained by Christ, have such relation to Him crucified, as that, truly, yet sacramentally only, they are sometimes called by the name of the things they represent, to wit, the body and blood of Christ; albeit in substance and nature they still remain truly and only bread and wine, as they were before.
Matt. 26:26-28; 1 Cor. 11:26-28; Matt. 26:29.

6. That doctrine which maintains a change of the substance of bread and wine into the substance of Christ's body and blood (commonly called transubstantiation) by consecration of a priest, or by any other way, is repugnant, not to Scripture alone, but even to common sense and reason; overthroweth the nature of the sacrament, and hath been, and is the cause of manifold superstitions; yea, of gross idolatries.
Acts 3:21 with 1 Cor. 11:24-26; Luke 24:6, 39.

7. Worthy receivers outwardly partaking of the visible elements in this sacrament, do then also, inwardly by faith, really and indeed, yet not carnally and corporally, but spiritually, receive and feed upon Christ crucified, and all benefits of His death: the body and blood of Christ being then, not corporally or carnally, in, with, or under the bread and wine; yet, as really, but spiritually, present to the faith of believers in that ordinance, as the elements themselves are to their outward senses.
1 Cor. 11:28; 1 Cor. 10:16.

4. Previous preparation, by self-examination, repentance of sin, meditation upon God's grace, and resolution of new obedience is required of those who make this profession of their union with Christ and love to Him.
1 Cor. 11:27-32; 1 Cor. 10:21-22.

8. Although ignorant and wicked men receive the outward elements in this sacrament: yet they receive not the thing signified thereby, but by their unworthy coming thereunto are guilty of the body and blood of the Lord to their own damnation. Wherefore, all ignorant and ungodly persons, as they are unfit to enjoy communion with Him, so are they unworthy of the Lord's table; and cannot, without great sin against Christ while they remain such, partake of these holy mysteries, or be admitted thereunto.
1 Cor. 11:27-29; 2 Cor. 6:14-16; 1 Cor. 5:6-7, 13; 2 Thess. 3:6, 14-15; Matt. 7:6.

5. The Lord's Supper is to be administered only to those who are accepted by the session dispensing the sacrament.

6. *We deny* that the individual is sole judge of his fitness to partake of the sacrament.
1 Cor. 5:1-13.

7. *We reject* the practice of offering the sacrament of Communion to any one who is not a member of the visible church.

Chapter 30: Of Church Censures

1. The Lord Jesus, as King and Head of His Church, hath therein appointed a government, in the hand of Church officers, distinct from the civil magistrate.
Isa. 9:6-7; 1 Tim. 5:17; 1 Thess. 5:12; Acts 20:17, 28; Heb. 13:7, 17, 24; 1 Cor. 12:28; Matt. 28:18-20.

2. To these officers, the keys of the kingdom of heaven are committed: by virtue whereof, they have power respectively to retain, and remit sins; to shut that kingdom against the impenitent, both by the Word and censures; and to open it unto penitent sinners, by the ministry of the Gospel, and by absolution from censures, as occasion shall require.
Matt. 16:19; Matt. 18:17-18; John 20:21-23; 2 Cor. 2:6-8.

3. Church censures are necessary, for the reclaiming and gaining of offending brethren, for deterring of others from the like offences, for purging out of that leaven which might infect the whole lump, for vindicating the honour of Christ, and the holy profession of the Gospel, and for preventing the wrath of God, which might justly fall upon the Church, if they should suffer His covenant and the seals thereof to be profaned by notorious and obstinate offenders.
1 Cor. 5; 1 Tim. 5:20; Matt. 7:6; 1 Tim. 1:20; 1 Cor. 11:27-34 with Jude 1:23.

1. Our Lord commanded church discipline, so no church which fails to exercise it where needed can hope for His blessing.
Matt. 18:18; Matt. 16:19; Rev. 2:2, 20.

2. Discipline is required by the organic nature of the Church.
1 Cor. 12:13, 25-26; 1 Cor. 5:1-13; Rev. 2:2.

3. There are many ways provided by the Lord to deal with offenses in the Church. Christians have a responsibility to admonish one another in the Lord. Some offenses may be resolved by informal counsel by one or more elders. Official discipline is to be administered by the courts of the Church, not by elders individually. Such counsel and discipline should be received in a spirit of Christian submission.
Matt. 18:15-17; Gal. 6:1; Col. 3:16; Col. 1:28.

4. For the better attaining of these ends, the officers of the Church are to proceed by admonition; suspension from the sacrament of the Lord's Supper for a season; and by excommunication from the Church; according to the nature of the crime, and demerit of the person.
1 Thess. 5:12; 2 Thess. 3:6, 14-15; 1 Cor. 5:4-5, 13; Matt. 18:17; Titus 3:10.

4. The authority and discipline of the Church extends to all members, irrespective of rank or station in life. Children who are baptized members are subject to that discipline.

5. Discipline should be exercised with prudence and discretion, in dependence upon the guidance of the Holy Spirit, with love both for the Lawgiver and lawbreaker.

6. *We reject* the view that a church member should be disciplined for everything at which another may be justly displeased.

(For specific details of discipline, see *Book of Discipline*.)

Chapter 31: Of Synods and Councils

(Larger Catechism: 123-133; Shorter Catechism: 63-66)

1. Christ is the only Head and Lawgiver of the Church. He gave the apostles authority to establish the permanent form of church government, which is set forth in the New Testament.
Eph. 1:22; Matt. 18:18; 1 Cor. 14:37; Eph. 4:11-12; 2 Cor. 13:10; Acts 14:23; Acts 20:17, 28; Heb. 13:17.

1. For the better government, and further edification of the Church, there ought to be such assemblies as are commonly called synods or councils.
Acts 15:2, 4, 6.

2. As magistrates may lawfully call a synod of ministers, and other fit persons, to consult and advise with, about matters of religion; so, if magistrates be open enemies to the Church, the ministers of Christ of themselves, by virtue of their office, or they, with other fit persons, upon delegation from their Churches, may meet together in such assemblies.
Isa. 49:23; 1 Tim. 2:1-2; 2 Chron. 19:8-11; 2 Chron. 29—30; Matt. 2:4-5; Prov. 11:14; Acts 15:2, 4, 22-23, 25.

2. *We reject* paragraph 2 of the *Confession of Faith*.

3. No ecclesiastical authority is placed in the hands of private Christians or civil rulers; church judicatories are subordinate only to Christ Jesus. They appoint, by an exclusive right, their own times and places of meeting and adjournment.
Matt. 22:21. (For details, see *Directory for Church Government,* chaps. 6-7.)

3. It belongeth to synods and councils, ministerially to determine controversies of faith and cases of conscience, to set down rules and directions for the better ordering of the public worship of God, and government of His Church; to receive complaints in cases of mal-administration, and authoritatively to determine the same: which decrees and determinations, if consonant to the Word of God, are to be received with reverence and submission; not only for their agreement with the Word, but also for the power whereby they are made, as being an ordinance of God appointed thereunto in His Word.
Acts 15:15, 19, 24, 27-31; Acts 16:4; Matt. 18:17-20.

4. *We reject* the systems of church government which center authority in one individual or in a hierarchy of bishops. *We further reject* the independent congregational system with authority vested in autonomous congregations.

4. All synods or councils, since the Apostles' times, whether general or particular, may err; and many have erred. Therefore they are not to be made the rule of faith or practice; but to be used as a help in both.
Eph. 2:20; Acts 17:11; 1 Cor. 2:5; 2 Cor. 1:24.

5. Subordinate standards, such as the *Confession of Faith, Catechisms* and the *Testimony,* serve a necessary and useful purpose as a summary of biblical teaching, a basis for fellowship and common service, and as a testimony to the world of the church's belief and practice. They are never to be taken as a substitute for God's Word or as a complete or final exposition of it.
Rom. 15:5-6; 1 Tim. 3:15-16; Heb. 4:12; Mark 7:6-13.

5. Synods and councils are to handle, or conclude, nothing, but that which is ecclesiastical: and are not to intermeddle with civil affairs which concern the commonwealth; unless by way of humble petition, in cases extraordinary; or by way of advice, for satisfaction of conscience, if they be thereunto required by the civil magistrate.
Luke 12:13-14; John 18:36.

6. It is the responsibility of the Church to declare God's Word to civil authorities as it applies to their use of the power that has been given them.
Acts 9:15; Ps. 119:46; Matt. 10:17-18; Luke 3:12-14. (Compare also the *Testimony,* chap. 23.)

Chapter 32
Of the State of Men After Death, And the Resurrection of the Dead

(Larger Catechism: 84-87; Shorter Catechism: 37-38)

1. The bodies of men, after death, return to dust and see corruption; but their souls (which neither die nor sleep) having an immortal subsistence, immediately return to God who gave them: the souls of the righteous, being then made perfect in holiness, are received into the highest heavens, where they behold the face of God, in light and glory, waiting for the full redemption of their bodies. And the souls of the wicked are cast into hell, where they remain in torments and utter darkness, reserved to the judgment of the great day. Beside these two places, for souls separated from their bodies, the Scripture acknowledgeth none.
Gen. 3:19; Acts 13:36; Luke 23:43; Eccl. 12:7; Heb. 12:23; 2 Cor. 5:1, 6, 8; Phil. 1:23 with Acts 3:21 and Eph. 4:10; Luke 16:23-24; Acts 1:25; Jude 1:6-7; 1 Pet. 3:19.

1. God has appointed to every man the time when he shall leave this world.
Ps. 39:4-5; Eccl. 3:2; Ps. 139:16.

2. *We reject* the idea of inactivity of the soul between death and resurrection called "soul sleep."
Eccl. 12:7; 2 Cor. 5:1-9.

3. *We reject* the teaching that there is a "second chance" of salvation after death.
Luke 16:22-26; Heb. 9:27; 2 Cor. 6:2; John 5:28-29; 2 Pet. 2:9.

4. *We reject* the teaching that there is a purgatory, where souls must be purified before entering heaven.
Luke 23:43; 2 Cor. 5:6, 8; Phil. 1:23.

2. At the last day, such as are found alive shall not die, but be changed: and all the dead shall be raised up, with the selfsame bodies and none other, although with different qualities, which shall be united again to their souls for ever.
1 Thess. 4:17; 1 Cor. 15:51-52; Job 19:26-27; 1 Cor. 15:42-44.

3. The bodies of the unjust shall, by the power of Christ, be raised to dishonour; the bodies of the just, by His Spirit, unto honour; and be made conformable to His own glorious body.
Acts 24:15; John 5:28-29; 1 Cor. 15:43; Phil. 3:21.

5. *We reject* the idea that the soul at death is, or can be, reincarnated in another human or animal form.
Eccl. 12:7; Heb. 9:27.

Chapter 33: Of the Last Judgment

(Larger Catechism: 56, 87-90; Shorter Catechism: 37-38)

1. The return of our Lord to earth is clearly taught in Scripture. He made many promises to return. His coming will be personal and visible. He will come in glory at a time unknown to man.
Rev. 22:7, 12, 20; John 14:3; Acts 1:11; Rev. 1:7; 1 Thess. 4:16; Matt. 16:27; Col. 3:4; Luke 12:40; Rev. 16:15; Mark 13:32-35; 1 Thess. 5:2.

2. At the time of Christ's second coming all the dead will be raised and the world will be judged.
John 5:28-29; 2 Thess. 1:7-10; Ps. 96:13; Ps. 98:9.

3. *We reject* the teaching that the Kingdom of God can only be brought in by Christ's return or that Christ is not now reigning as King over all things.
Matt. 28:18; Eph. 1:20-22; Phil. 2:9-11; Col. 1:18.

1. God hath appointed a day, wherein He will judge the world in righteousness, by Jesus Christ, to whom all power and judgment is given of the Father. In which day, not only the apostate angels shall be judged, but likewise all persons that have lived upon earth shall appear before the tribunal of Christ, to give an account of their thoughts, words, and deeds; and to receive according to what they have done in the body, whether good or evil.
Acts 17:31; John 5:22, 27; 1 Cor. 6:3; Jude 1:6; 2 Pet. 2:4; 2 Cor. 5:10; Eccl. 12:14; Rom. 2:16; Rom. 14:10, 12; Matt. 12:36-37.

4. The final judgment for the Christian will be an assessment of his obedience to God and of his stewardship of the gifts and talents God has committed to his care. Whatever is imperfect will be burned away, and his faithfulness will be rewarded.
2 Cor. 5:10; Rom. 14:10-12; 1 Cor. 3:9-15; 1 Cor. 4:5; Matt. 25:14-40.

2. The end of God's appointing this day is for the manifestation of the glory of His mercy, in the eternal salvation of the elect; and of His justice, in the damnation of the reprobate who are wicked and disobedient. For then shall the righteous go into everlasting life, and receive that fulness of joy and refreshing, which shall come from the presence of the Lord: but the wicked, who know not God, and obey not the Gospel of Jesus Christ, shall be cast into eternal torments, and be punished with everlasting destruction from the presence of the Lord, and from the glory of His power.
Matt. 25:31-46; Rom. 2:5-6; Rom. 9:22-23; Matt. 25:21; Acts 3:19; 2 Thess. 1:7-10.

3. As Christ would have us to be certainly persuaded that there shall be a day of judgment, both to deter all men from sin, and for the greater consolation of the godly in their adversity; so will He have that day unknown to men, that they may shake off all carnal security, and be always watchful, because they know not at what hour the Lord will come; and may be ever prepared to say, Come, Lord Jesus, come quickly, Amen.
2 Pet. 3:11, 14; 2 Cor. 5:10-11; 2 Thess. 1:5-7; Luke 21:27-28; Rom. 8:23-25; Matt. 24:36, 42-44; Mark 13:35-37; Luke 12:35-36; Rev. 22:20.

5. Believers are to look forward eagerly to the last great day, in which they will share in Christ's final victory over evil and experience the fulness of joy which is found in the presence of God, forever.
2 Pet. 3:11-13; Ps. 16:11.